Essential Maths 7S

Homework Book

Michael White

Elmwood Press

First published 2008 by
Elmwood Press
80 Attimore Road
Welwyn Garden City
Herts. AL8 6LP
Tel. 01707 333232

ISBN 9781 906 622 022

Typeset and illustrated by Domex e-Data Pvt. Ltd.
Printed and bound by WS Bookwell

Contents

UNIT 1

SQUARE NUMBERS ————————————————————

M

1 A   B 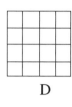 C D 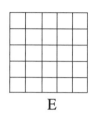 E

(a) Draw squares A, B, C, D and E in your book. Square A has 1 small square. Square B has 4 small squares.

(b) Write down how many small squares there are in squares C, D and E.

2 Draw one large square using exactly 36 small squares.

E

1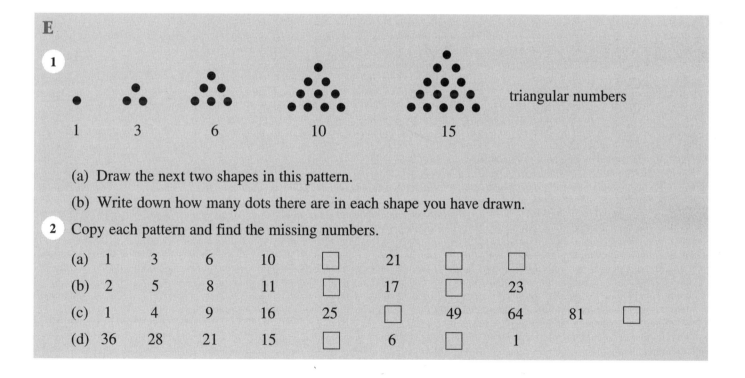

(a) Draw the next two shapes in this pattern.

(b) Write down how many dots there are in each shape you have drawn.

2 Copy each pattern and find the missing numbers.

(a) 1   3   6   10   ☐   21   ☐   ☐

(b) 2   5   8   11   ☐   17   ☐   23

(c) 1   4   9   16   25   ☐   49   64   81   ☐

(d) 36   28   21   15   ☐   6   ☐   1

M

Copy and complete by filling in the boxes.

1 6 9 12 15 ☐ ☐   **2** 5 8 11 14 ☐ ☐

3 4 9 14 19 ☐ ☐   **4** 3 9 15 21 ☐ ☐

5 27 24 21 18 ☐ ☐   **6** 25 23 21 19 ☐ ☐

7 3 7 11 15 ☐ ☐   **8** 39 34 29 24 ☐ ☐

Copy the sequences and write the next three numbers. What is the rule for each sequence?

9 23 28 33 38   **10** 17 27 37 47   **11** 42 40 38 36

12 55 50 45 40   **13** 646 546 446 346   **14** 20 50 80 110

15 56 59 62 65   **16** 5 $5\frac{1}{2}$ 6 $6\frac{1}{2}$

E

Write the first five numbers in each sequence.

	Start at	Rule		Start at	Rule
1	17	Add 4	**2**	19	Add 15
3	13	Add 9	**4**	70	Subtract 6
5	90	Add 40	**6**	13	Add 25
7	57	Subtract 8	**8**	290	Subtract 20
9	96	Subtract 12	**10**	30	Add 19

Questions **11** to **18** are sequences with negative numbers. Copy and complete by filling in the boxes.

11 4 3 2 1 0 –1 ☐ –3 ☐ ☐

12 –6 –5 –4 ☐ ☐ ☐ 0 1 ☐ ☐

13 8 6 4 ☐ 0 –2 ☐ ☐ ☐

14 0 –1 ☐ ☐ –4 ☐ –6 ☐

15 –9 –7 ☐ ☐ –1 ☐ 3 5 ☐

16 –10 –8 ☐ –4 ☐ ☐ 2 ☐ ☐

17 7 5 3 ☐ ☐ –3 –5 ☐ ☐

18 8 5 2 ☐ –4 –7 ☐ ☐

M

b	burger	85p
s	soup	70p
c	chips	95p
p	pizza	95p
r	roll	50p

This menu is in a café.
If somebody orders chips and 2 burgers,
the waiter writes $c + 2b$.

Use the short way to write down each of these orders:

1 1 burger and 1 chips.

2 2 pizzas and 2 chips.

3 3 chips, 2 burgers and 1 soup.

4 3 burgers, 2 chips and 2 rolls.

5 4 soups and 3 rolls.

6 2 burgers, 3 chips and 2 pizzas.

7 2 chips, 1 soup, 3 burgers and 1 roll.

8 2 pizzas, 2 chips, 1 burger and 1 soup.

For each order below, work out the cost in money.

> Example: $2c$ means $2 \times c$ which is $2 \times 95p = 190p$
> $2c + r$ costs $190p + 50p = 240p = £2.40$

9 $b + c$

10 $b + c + r$

11 $c + p$

12 $3s$

13 $2p$

14 $2p + c$

15 $2b + 2c$

16 $p + 2c + 2r$

17 $3c + 4r$

E

Another café has this menu. Use the short way to write down each of the following orders:

f	fish	£2.80
c	chips	95p
p	pie	£1.35
s	sausage	65p
t	tea	80p
l	lemonade	75p

> Example: $2f + 3t$ for 2 fish and 3 teas

1 One pie and one chips.

2 Two sausages, one chips and one tea.

3 Two fish, two chips and two lemonades.

4 Three chips, two pies, one sausage and one lemonade.

5 Four fish, two sausages, five chips and three lemonades.

6 Three fish, two pies, three chips and three teas.

More questions are on the next page.

For each order, work out the cost in money.

7 $c + p + l$

8 $2f + 2c$

9 $p + 2c + 2t$

10 $2s + c + l$

11 $2p + f + 3c$

12 $4s + 2c + 2l$

13 $2f + 3c + p$

14 $2s + 2p + 3c + 2t$

15 $3f + 3c + 2t + l$

PRIME NUMBERS 1 ⎯⎯⎯⎯⎯⎯⎯⎯⎯⎯⎯⎯⎯⎯⎯ **Main Book page 6**

> A prime number can only be divided exactly by two different numbers (these are the numbers 1 and itself).
>
> 1 is **not** a prime number.

M

1 Which of these divisions have no remainder?

(a) $8 \div 1$　　(b) $8 \div 2$　　(c) $8 \div 3$　　(d) $8 \div 4$
(e) $8 \div 5$　　(f) $8 \div 6$　　(g) $8 \div 7$　　(h) $8 \div 8$

Is 8 a prime number? (ie. can 8 only be divided exactly by 1 and itself?)

2 Which of these divisions have no remainder?

(a) $11 \div 1$　　(b) $11 \div 2$　　(c) $11 \div 3$　　(d) $11 \div 4$
(e) $11 \div 5$　　(f) $11 \div 6$　　(g) $11 \div 7$　　(h) $11 \div 8$
(i) $11 \div 9$　　(j) $11 \div 10$　　(k) $11 \div 11$

Is 11 a prime number? (ie. can 11 only be divided exactly by 1 and itself?)

3 Is 13 a prime number?　　　　**4** Is 12 a prime number?

E

1 Write down the prime number in each group.

(a) 4, 5, 6　　(b) 18, 19, 20　　(c) 23, 24, 25
(d) 16, 17, 18　　(e) 9, 10, 11　　(f) 28, 29, 30

2 Write down all the prime numbers shown below.

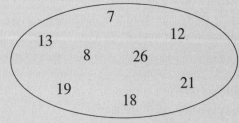

3 Write down all the prime numbers between 30 and 40.

MENTAL STRATEGIES 1 (+ AND –) ────────────────

M

Copy and complete the squares.

1

+	7	5	8
8	15		
6			
9			

2

+	16	24	49
13			
36			85
48			

3

–	8	6	9
27	19		
29			
35			

4

–	27	25	19
68		43	
49			
37			

Write the answers only.

5 $65 - 40$ **6** $258 + 9$ **7** $130 + 90$ **8** $98 - 9$

9 $100 - 11$ **10** $47 - 8$ **11** $51 - 7$ **12** $190 + 60$

E

Copy and complete by writing the missing number in the box.

1 $300 + \boxed{} = 635$ **2** $740 - \boxed{} = 430$ **3** $380 - \boxed{} = 290$

4 $\boxed{} + 390 = 640$ **5** $375 - \boxed{} = 160$ **6** $\boxed{} - 400 = 259$

7 $320 - \boxed{} = 180$ **8** $3.7 + \boxed{} = 4$ **9** $849 - \boxed{} = 450$

10 $\boxed{} + 373 = 400$ **11** $789 - \boxed{} = 149$ **12** $3.6 + \boxed{} = 10$

13 $7.1 - \boxed{} = 4.9$ **14** $258 + \boxed{} = 400$ **15** $\boxed{} + 499 = 1002.$

M

What do you need to add to each number to make 100?

1 78 **2** 49 **3** 83 **4** 68 **5** 31 **6** 18

What do you need to add to each number to make 1000?

7 150 **8** 250 **9** 300 **10** 550 **11** 875 **12** 725

Match up each question below with the correct answer, for example: question **13** matches answer D.

13 4×6 **14** 9×6 **15** 5×9

16 $12 \div 6$ **17** $30 \div 6$ **18** 8×9

19 $27 \div 9$ **20** 10×6 **21** 7×9

A	B	C
63	54	3

D	E	F
24	2	5

G	H	I
72	45	60

E

Match up each question below with the correct answer, for example: question **1** matches answer H.

1 4×7 **2** 6×8 **3** 5×8

4 $35 \div 7$ **5** $48 \div 8$ **6** $64 \div 8$

7 8×3 **8** 8×7 **9** 7×2

10 8×0 **11** $32 \div 8$ **12** $63 \div 7$

A	B	C
5	8	4

D	E	F
48	56	6

G	H	I
0	28	40

J	K	L
24	9	14

Copy and complete:

13 $9 \times \square = 54$ **14** $9 \times \square = 45$ **15** $\square \div 9 = 7$ **16** $\square \div 9 = 9$

17 $6 \times \square = 48$ **18** $6 \times \square = 24$ **19** $\square \div 6 = 9$ **20** $\square \div 6 = 6$

21 Dan has 9 boxes. Each box has 7 packets of paper in it. How many packets of paper does Dan have?

M

Write the numbers on these cards in words.

1 [12] 2 [16] 3 [23] 4 [50] 5 [11]

6 [40] 7 [31] 8 [65] 9 [72] 10 [94]

11 [100] 12 [170] 13 [219] 14 [417] 15 [653]

Write the numbers below like the cards above.

16 fifteen 17 thirty-eight 18 forty-nine

19 ninety-one 20 twenty-six 21 two hundred and ten

22 three hundred and sixteen 23 four hundred and thirty-five

24 six hundred and forty-eight 25 two hundred and fifty-seven

E

Each month ten people earn the money shown below. Write this money in words.

1 Carla £633 2 Fergus £2416

3 Lee £1108 4 Sarah £983

5 Kat £2400 6 Imran £2968

7 Peter £1890 8 Molly £4116

9 Shamina £3127 10 James £1860

11 [4] [6] [1] [8] Make the largest number you can using these four cards.
Write your number (a) in figures
(b) in words.

12 Use the four cards in question 11 to make the smallest number you can.
Write your number (a) in figures
(b) in words.

M

1 Subtract 8 from 66.

2 Take 9 from 32.

3 What is 29 less than 51?

4 What is 120 take away 25?

Copy and complete:

5 $300 - \square = 210$ **6** $\square - 500 = 350$ **7** $\square - 65 = 200$ **8** $\square - 19 = 63$

9 The sum of 59 and 16 is $\square$.   **10** 87 plus 14 equals $\square$.

11 The total of 89 and 99 is $\square$.   **12** The sum of 36 and $\square$ is 75.

13 Add 49 to $\square$ to make 399.   **14** 50 plus $\square$ equals 124.

15 36 and 36 altogether is $\square$.   **16** The total of 110 and $\square$ is 201.

17 $214 - \square = 104$ **18** $\square - 80 = 126$

E

Copy and complete:

1 $57 + \square = 100$ **2** $130 + \square = 176$ **3** $\square + 37 = 200$ **4** $\square + 83 = 164$

5 $148 + \square = 185$ **6** $314 + \square = 400$ **7** $500 - \square = 422$ **8** $386 - \square = 250$

9 $\square - 85 = 115$ **10** $\square + 65 = 140$ **11** $49 + \square = 152$ **12** $\square + 750 = 2000$

Find the sum of the numbers in each question below:

13 164   89   **14** 206   38   419   **15** 99   126   150.

Find the difference between each pair of numbers below:

16 201   39   **17** 360   190   **18** 387   70   **19** 93   47

20 161   98   **21** 3002   13

M

1. Add 10 onto   (a) 38   (b) 277   (c) 94   (d) 372

2. Add 40 onto   (a) 34   (b) 70   (c) 138   (d) 88

3. Take 10 from   (a) 89   (b) 264   (c) 319   (d) 208

4. Take 80 from   (a) 145   (b) 132   (c) 192   (d) 212

Copy and complete:

5. $135 + \square = 200$ 6. $218 + \square = 418$ 7. $265 + \square = 300$ 8. $465 - \square = 265$

9. $900 - \square = 50$ 10. $1400 - \square = 800$

11. Start with 30. Keep adding 40. Write down the first six numbers you get.

12. Start with 420. Keep subtracting 50. Write down the first six numbers you get.

E

1. Add 80 onto   (a) 365   (b) 293   (c) 316   (d) 453

2. Subtract 90 from   (a) 352   (b) 625   (c) 417   (d) 509

Copy and complete:

3. $329 + \square = 400$ 4. $1700 + \square = 3000$ 5. $284 + \square = 400$ 6. $562 + \square = 600$

7. $3200 + \square = 4000$ 8. $617 + \square = 800$ 9. $3000 - \square = 2250$ 10. $6300 - \square = 5950$

11. $3150 - \square = 2050$

Copy and complete these number chains:

12. $\boxed{0} \xrightarrow{+0} \square \xrightarrow{+0} \square \xrightarrow{+0} \square \xrightarrow{+0} \square$

13. $\boxed{8} \xrightarrow{+0} \square \xrightarrow{+0} \square \xrightarrow{-0} \square \xrightarrow{-0} \square \xrightarrow{+80} \square$

14. $\boxed{0} \xrightarrow{+0} \square \xrightarrow{+0} \square \xrightarrow{-0} \square \xrightarrow{+80} \square \xrightarrow{+0} \square$

M

-10 -9 -8 -7 -6 -5 -4 -3 -2 -1 0 1 2 3 4 5 6 7 8 9 10

1 Find the difference between

(a) -6 and 2   (b) -7 and -2   (c) -4 and 3

(d) -2 and 3   (e) -8 and -3   (f) -2 and 5

2 Which temperature is the coldest? | -3°C | | 0°C | | -5°C |

3 Put these numbers in order, smallest first.

(a)
-2	1	0
-3	2	

(b)
4	-2	1
-3	-4	

(c)
-1	4	-5
1	-2	

4 Copy and complete the table below.

Temperature °C	Change °C	New temperature °C
4	falls by 5	
-3	rises by 6	
-6	rises by 2	
-9	falls by 1	
3	falls by 6	
-2	rises by 4	

5 What must you add to -7 to make -1?

E

1 The temperature in Nottingham is -2°C.

(a) What is the temperature if it rises by 6°C?

(b) What is the temperature if it drops by 2°C?

2 Copy and complete the tables showing changes in temperature.

(a)
Old	Change	New
-3°C	+5°C	2°C
4°C	-7°C	
-6°C	-2°C	
5°C	-6°C	
1°C	-4°C	
-9°C	+4°C	

(b)
Old	Change	New
2°C	-6°C	-4°C
	+5°C	1°C
	-4°C	-2°C
	-6°C	-5°C
	+8°C	3°C
	-1°C	-1°C

(c)
Old	Change	New
6°C	-8°C	-2°C
4°C		-3°C
-3°C		-1°C
-7°C		-5°C
5°C		0°C
-1°C		-6°C

ADDITION AND SUBTRACTION ————————————

M

Copy and complete

1   36
    + 29

2   43
    + 38

3   68
    + 25

4   54
    + 38

5   73
    + 74

6   87
    + 69

7   124
    + 37

8   146
    + 36

9   246
    + 84

10   268
    + 94

11   64
    − 38

12   53
    − 25

13   72
    − 49

14   86
    − 47

15   73
    − 28

16   43
    − 18

17   61
    − 46

18   73
    − 57

19   84
    − 57

20   92
    − 65

E

Work out

1 176 + 59

2 263 + 48

3 219 + 67

4 408 + 73

5 137 + 48 + 37

6 316 + 136 + 74

7 536 + 102 + 78

8 Find the difference between each pair of numbers below:

    (a) 184 and 36   (b) 253 and 45   (c) 217 and 88

    (d) 516 and 67   (e) 438 and 54   (f) 525 and 87

9 Jack has collected 58 football cards. There are 94 cards in a full set. How many more cards does Jack need to collect to make a full set?

10 Copy and complete the addition square.

+	9			
15	24			
		50	63	
26		39		51
	45			

ADDING AND SUBTRACTING DECIMALS

M

Copy and complete.

1) £2.64
  + £0.58

2) £3.18
  + £0.49

3) £4.77
  + £1.36

4) £2.84
  + £0.68

Workout

5) £3.29 + 46p

6) £4.36 + 87p + 39p

7) £4.18 + 74p + 58p

8) £7.41 + 86p

9) £5.22 + £1.19 + 63p

10) £8.16 + 38p + 75p

Copy and complete.

11) £4.18
   – £0.37

12) £3.64
   – £1.89

13) £4.28
   – £1.75

14) £2.73
   – £1.49

E

Work out

1) £4.33 – £1.85

2) £6.51 – £4.38

3) £3.44 – £2.63

4) £6.50 – £2.87

5) £4.23 – £1.74

6) £5.16 – £2.69

7) Mel has £6.15. She spends £3.83. How much money does she have left?

8) Hal buys a drink for £1.36. How much change will he get from a £5 note?

Work out

9) 13 + 0.47

10) 3.6 + 6.19

11) 3.2 – 1.9

12) 9 – 6.8

13) 0.3 + 5 + 2.14

14) 17.6 + 3.82 + 4

15) 16.4 – 11.7

16) 5.4 – 2.16

17) 19 – 5.82

18) Find the number which belongs in each empty box.

(a) $1.8 + \boxed{} = 3.25$

(b) $\boxed{} + 1.87 = 12$

MENTAL STRATEGIES (× AND ÷)

M

Write the answers only.

1 3×10 **2** 8×1 **3** 7×10 **4** $50 \div 10$ **5** 4×100

6 $2 \div 1$ **7** $900 \div 100$ **8** $40 \div 10$

Copy and complete.

9 $2 \times \square = 200$ **10** $6 \times \square = 60$ **11** $\square \times 1 = 9$ **12** $\square \times 100 = 500$

13 $\square \times 1 = 3$ **14** $7 \times \square = 700$ **15** $\square \div 1 = 6$ **16** $\square \div 100 = 8$

17 $\square \div 10 = 3$ **18** $700 \div \square = 7$ **19** $50 \div \square = 5$ **20** $4 \div \square = 4$

E

Write the answers only.

1 24×10 **2** 38×1 **3** 14×100 **4** 39×10

5 $360 \div 10$ **6** $5200 \div 100$ **7** $690 \div 1$ **8** $2700 \div 100$

Copy and complete.

9 $46 \times \square = 460$ **10** $33 \times \square = 33$ **11** $29 \times \square = 2900$

12 $73 \times \square = 7300$ **13** $810 \div \square = 81$ **14** $3500 \div \square = 35$

15 $6800 \div \square = 680$ **16** $\square \div 10 = 43$ **17** $\square \div 100 = 19$

18 $\square \div 1 = 47$ **19** $\square \times 100 = 8400$ **20** $\square \times 10 = 7100$

21 Copy and complete the following

(a) $\boxed{17} \xrightarrow{\times 100} \boxed{} \xrightarrow{\div 10} \boxed{} \xrightarrow{\times 100} \boxed{}$

(b) $\boxed{34} \xrightarrow{\times 100} \boxed{} \xrightarrow{\times 10} \boxed{} \xrightarrow{\div 100} \boxed{}$

(c) $\boxed{} \xrightarrow{\times 10} \boxed{} \xrightarrow{\times 10} \boxed{} \xrightarrow{\div 100} \boxed{49}$

Remember: for money £3.70 on a calculator may show as 3.7

M

Use a calculator to work out

1 8 – 14   **2** 7 – 19   **3** 38 – 19   **4** 16 – 32

5 7 – 43   **6** 106 – 39   **7** 14 – 16   **8** 13 – 46

Now do these (be careful!)

9 £6.20 – 45p   **10** £5.09 – 63p   **11** £3.76 + 65p

12 £3.48 + £1.39   **13** £4.38 + £2.49   **14** £8.14 + £1.59

Now use brackets as shown

15 6 × (42 – 29)   **16** 18 × (7 – 5)   **17** 43 + (7 × 13)

18 20 ÷ (2 + 3)   **19** 41 × (17 – 16)   **20** 100 ÷ (43 – 18)

E

1 Each day a squirrel collects 23 nuts but eats 4 of them. How many nuts will the squirrel have after 25 days?

2 Use a calculator to copy and complete:

(a) 39 + ☐ = 118   (b) 76 + ☐ = 137   (c) ☐ + 173 = 220

(d) ☐ + 149 = 302   (e) 316 – ☐ = 177   (f) 284 – ☐ = 95

(g) ☐ – 146 = 83   (h) ☐ + 212 = 408   (i) 324 + ☐ = 600

(j) ☐ – 258 = 124   (k) 429 – ☐ = 36   (l) 304 – ☐ = 196

3 The temperature in Ascot is 16°C. It falls by 21°C. What is the new temperature?

4 'consecutive' numbers are numbers which follow each other.

(a) Find 2 consecutive numbers which multiply together to make 156.

(b) Find 4 consecutive numbers which add together to make 38.

M

1. What is 5 times 20?

2. Multiply 4 by 6.

3. Find 4 lots of 30.

4. Find the product of 9 and 3.

5. Will feeds his fish 4 times each week. How many times does he feed them during 7 weeks?

6. What is 64 multiplied by 100?

7. How many days are there in 3 weeks?

8. Divide 36 by 4.

9. Share 26 by 2.

10. How many 5s make 45?

11. What is 18 divided by 3?

12. Jackie shares 32 sweets between 4 children. How many sweets does each child get?

E

1. An 80 cm piece of wood is cut into 5 equal parts. How long is each part?

2. A bus can take 50 people. How many buses are needed to take 250 people?

3. A dog chews 3 letters each day. How many letters would the dog chew in 2 weeks?

4. Don checks 28 litter bins. 1 in every 4 of the bins is full. How many bins are full?

5. A box of chocolates has 25 chocolates. How many chocolates are there in 7 boxes?

6. A teacher has to split a class of 24 children into groups of 3. How many groups will there be?

7. (a) What is the smallest number multiplied by itself?

   (b) Which number is five times the second smallest number?

   (c) Six different products can be made using pairs of the four numbers. Can you find them all?

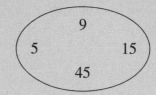

MEASURING LENGTH ──────────────── **Main Book page 24**

M

1 Read the measurements shown.

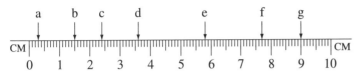

Measure these lines.

2 ─────────────────

3 ──────────────────────

4 ──────────────────

5 ──────────────────────────

6 ────────────────────────────

7 ──────────────────────

8 ────────────────────────────────────

9 ──────────────────────────

10 ─────────────────────────────────

E

1 Read the measurements shown.

Measure these lines.

2

3

4

5

6

METRIC UNITS OF LENGTH ────────────────────────

Remember: 1 metre = 100 cm   1 kilometre = 1000 m

M

For each question below, is it more sensible to measure using mm, cm, m or km?

1 height of a house   **2** width of a matchstick   **3** length of a book

4 length of a fork   **5** length of England   **6** height of a mountain

7 Make up to 1 metre.

(a) 25 cm + ☐   (b) 45 cm + ☐   (c) ☐ + 23 cm   (d) ☐ + 69 cm

8 Make up to 1 kilometre.

(a) 700 m + ☐   (b) 400 m + ☐   (c) ☐ + 250 m

(d) ☐ + 650 m   (e) ☐ + 875 m   (f) 930 m + ☐

9 Make up to 1 metre.

(a) 86 cm + ☐   (b) 39 cm + ☐   (c) ☐ + 47 cm   (d) ☐ + 72 cm

E

1 Write down two things you would measure using:

(a) metres   (b) kilometres   (c) centimetres

2 Copy and complete.

(a) 4 km = ☐ m   (b) 6 km = ☐ m   (c) $\frac{1}{2}$ km = ☐ m

(d) 8 m = ☐ cm   (e) 4 m = ☐ cm   (f) 200 cm = ☐ m

(g) 900 cm = ☐ m   (h) 150 cm = ☐ m   (i) 3000 m = ☐ km

(j) 7000 m = ☐ km   (k) 50 cm = ☐ m   (l) 2500 m = ☐ km

3 Which is larger?   (300 cm) or (4 m)

4 Which is larger?   (600 m) or ($\frac{1}{2}$ km)

5 Which is larger?   ($\frac{1}{4}$ m) or (23 cm)

M

Measure each side of each shape and work out the perimeter.

1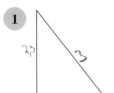

2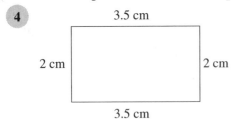

3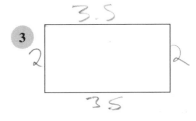

Work out the perimeter of each shape below.

4
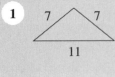
3.5 cm
2 cm   2 cm
3.5 cm

5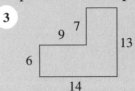
2.4 cm   4.3 cm
2.1 cm
5.6 cm

6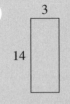
1.5 cm
1.9 cm
3.2 cm
1.9 cm
1.5 cm

7 Work out the perimeter of a rectangle with sides 4 cm and 9 cm.

8 Work out the perimeter of a square where each of its sides is 2.5 cm.

E

The lengths of these shapes are in cm. For each shape work out the perimeter.

1
7   7
11

2
13
10   4
8
6
5

3
9 7
6   13
14

4
3
14

5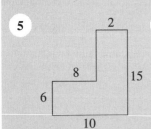
2
8
6
10

6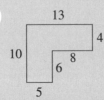
3
4   4
4   4
3

7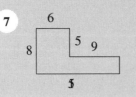
6
8   5 9
5

8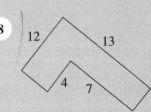
12   13
4   7

9 Copy and complete this table showing the measurements of rectangles.

length	7 cm	10 cm		12 cm	30 cm
width	5 cm	6 cm	3 cm		
perimeter			16 cm	34 cm	76 cm

M

Find the area of each rectangle.

1
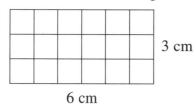
3 cm

6 cm

2
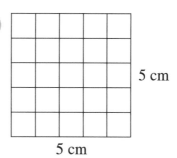
5 cm

5 cm

3
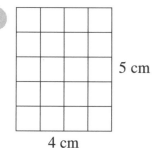
5 cm

4 cm

4
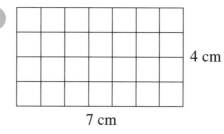
4 cm

7 cm

5
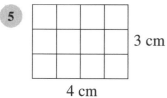
3 cm

4 cm

6
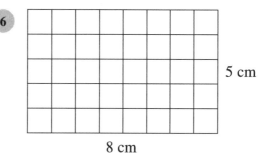
5 cm

8 cm

7 Draw a square with sides of 6 cm. Find its area.

8 Draw a rectangle with a length of 7 cm and an area of 35 cm². Work out its perimeter.

E

Work out the areas of these shapes by counting squares and half squares.

1
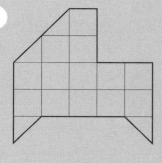

2
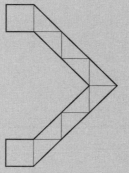

3
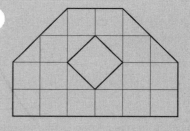

4 Draw at least 3 shapes of your own on squared paper. Work out the area of each of your shapes.

AREA AND PERIMETER ————————————————

M

1 Calculate the perimeter of each rectangle. All lengths are in cm.

(a)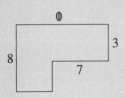

(b)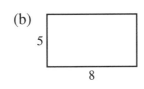

(c)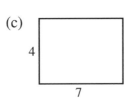

(d)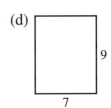

2 Calculate the area of each rectangle in question **1** above.

3 Copy and complete this table showing the measurements of rectangles.

length	6 cm	8 cm	4 cm	10 cm	
width	9 cm	7 cm	2 cm		5 cm
perimeter					
area				70 cm²	30 cm²

E

1 On squared paper draw three different rectangles each with an area of 12 cm².
Work out the perimeter of each rectangle.

2 The lengths of these shapes are in cm. Work out the area of each shape.

(a)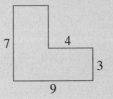

(b)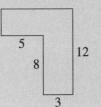

(c)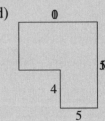

(d)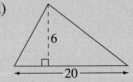

3 Work out the perimeter of each shape in question **2** .

4 Work out the area of each triangle. All the lengths are in cm.

(a)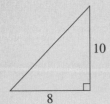

(b)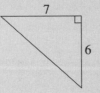

(c)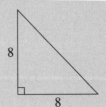

(d)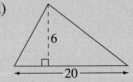

THREE DIMENSIONAL SHAPES ━━━━━━━━━━━━━━━━━━━ **Main Book page 30**

M

Write down the name of each shape.

1 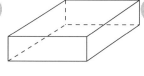 **2**   **3**  **4**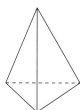

5 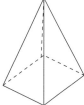 **6** 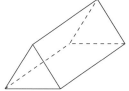 **7**   **8**

9 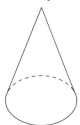 **10** 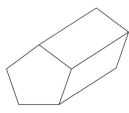 **11**  **12**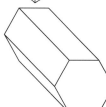

13 Which shapes above only have flat faces?

14 Which shape above has 4 vertices only?

15 Which shapes above have 6 faces only?

E

1 How many vertices does a cuboid have?

2 How many faces does a hexagonal prism have?

3 How many edges does a cuboid have?

4 Draw a triangular prism. How many vertices does a triangular prism have?

5 How many edges does a square based pyramid have?

6 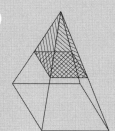 The top of this pyramid (shaded part) is cut off.

Look at the remaining bottom part. How many faces. vertices and edges does this part have?

M

For each set of data below, find:

    (a) the range   (b) the mode   (c) the median

1 The number of pets of seven children.

    3   7   1   3   5   4   6

2 The ages of nine children.

    11   12   15   12   9   9   8   12   8

3 The number of drinks taken by Joel during one week.

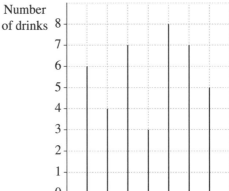

E

For each set of data below, find:

    (a) the range   (b) the mode   (c) the median   (d) the mean

1 The number of children in nine families.

    3   4   2   3   0   1   3   0   2

2 The number of homeworks during one week for 11 children

    4   10   8   2   7   4   7   8   4   4   8

3 The number of absences during 10 weeks for class 7A.

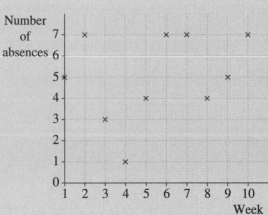

Unit 2

THE FOUR OPERATIONS 1 — **Main Book page 41**

M

What number belongs in the empty box?

1. ☐ → +4 → 7
2. ☐ → +8 → 13
3. ☐ → +7 → 10
4. ☐ → +9 → 15
5. ☐ → +3 → 12
6. ☐ → −5 → 4
7. ☐ → −6 → 10
8. ☐ → −7 → 12
9. ☐ → −4 → 14
10. ☐ → −8 → 9
11. ☐ → ×3 → 6
12. ☐ → ×5 → 20
13. ☐ → ×4 → 16
14. ☐ → ×10 → 40
15. ☐ → ×6 → 18
16. ☐ → ÷3 → 4
17. ☐ → ÷2 → 6
18. ☐ → ÷5 → 5
19. ☐ → ÷10 → 3
20. ☐ → ÷4 → 2

E

What number belongs in the empty box?

1. ☐ → −9 → 13
2. ☐ → +17 → 31
3. ☐ → +13 → 26
4. ☐ → −12 → 20
5. ☐ → +24 → 40
6. ☐ → −11 → 28
7. ☐ → −20 → 19
8. ☐ → −15 → 32
9. ☐ → +25 → 39
10. ☐ → +36 → 53
11. ☐ → ×7 → 42
12. ☐ → ×8 → 72
13. ☐ → ÷8 → 4
14. ☐ → ×11 → 55
15. ☐ → ÷9 → 6
16. ☐ → ÷8 → 6
17. ☐ → ×7 → 28
18. ☐ → ×9 → 63
19. ☐ → ÷11 → 8
20. ☐ → ÷7 → 8

M/E

1 This pictogram shows how many children in class 7B ate an apple during the school week.

Monday 🍎 🍎 🍎 🍎

Tuesday 🍎 🍎 🍎 🍎 🍎

Wednesday 🍎 🍎 🍎

Thursday 🍎 🍎 🍎 🍎 🍎 🍎

Friday 🍎 🍎

🍎 represents 3 children

(a) How many children ate apples on Wednesday?

(b) How many more children ate apples on Thursday than on Monday?

(c) On which day did least children eat an apple?

(d) How many fewer children ate an apple on Wednesday than on Tuesday?

2 This graph shows the number of children attending a football club each week.

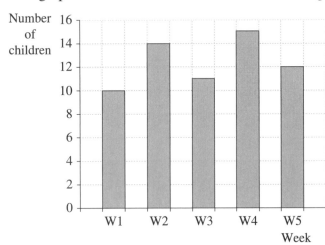

(a) How many children went to football club in week 2?

(b) How many children went to football club in week 3?

(c) How many more children went to football club in week 4 than in week 1?

(d) How many children went to football club in total during weeks 1 to 5?

3 The children in class 7A were asked what their favourite subject was, English (E), Maths (M), PE (P), Art (A) or History (H). These are the results.

A	M	P	H	A	E	M	M	A	P
H	E	A	P	H	H	E	P	H	M
M	A	P	P	E	M	A	A	P	A

Copy and complete the frequency table and then draw a bar chart to show the results.

subject	tally	frequency
E	||||	4
M		
P		
A		
H		

PROBABILITY 1 ─────────────────────────────

M

For each of these statements write one of these probabilities.

impossible   unlikely   even chance   likely   certain

1 When a coin is tossed it will show 'tails'.

2 The sun will rise tomorrow.

3 You will blink your eyes in the next minute.

4 Your next Christmas present will be delivered by a snowman.

5 You roll a dice and get an odd number.

6 It will rain in November.

7 You will be captured by aliens tonight.

8 You will be given homework in the next 3 months.

E

Draw the probability scale.

impossible   unlikely   evens   likely   certain

Draw an arrow on the scale to show the chance of each event below happening.

1 The day after Monday will be Tuesday.

2 You will grow an extra leg tonight then win the next Olympics 100 m race.

3 England will win the next World Cup at football.

4 You will get at least one birthday card when you have your next birthday.

5 Your maths teacher has a black belt in Judo.

6 When a coin is tossed it will show 'heads'.

7 You will find a tarantula in your bed tonight

8 In the next TV series, Doctor Who will defeat the aliens and save the planet.

M

1 What is the probability that each spinner will land on a shaded part?

(a)   (b)   (c)   (d)

2 There are four identical beads in a bag. I take out one bead.

(a) What is the probability of taking out A?

(b) What is the probability of taking out M?

3 Work out the probability of spinning a coin and getting 'tails'.

4 Using this spinner, what is the probability of getting:

(a) the number 7   (b) the number 5?

E

1 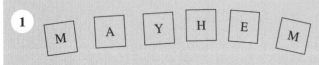 Tania shuffles these cards then picks one out. What is the probability that she picks:

(a) The letter H   (b) The letter M

(c) A vowel

2 These 7 balls are mixed up in a bag. Rosa picks out one ball. What is the probability that she picks:

(a) ■   (b) ★   (c) ▲

3 There are 17 beads in a bag. 8 beads are red, 5 beads are blue and 4 beads are green. I take out one bead. Find the probability of:

(a) taking out a green bead.   (b) taking out a red or blue bead.

(c) taking out a white bead.   (d) taking out a red or green bead.

4 There are eleven balls in a bucket. I take out one ball. What is the probability of taking out:

(a)   (b)   (c) or ?

M

What fraction of each shape is shaded?

1 **2** **3** 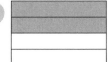 **4** **5**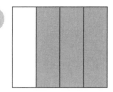

6 Copy and complete these sentences by writing the fractions in words.

(a) [　　　] of these shapes are stars.

(b) [　　　] of these shapes are circles.

(c) [　　　] of these shapes are *not* circles.

(d) [　　　] of these shapes are *not* stars.

7 Copy each grid.

(a)

Shade $\frac{3}{4}$ of the squares.

(b)

Shade $\frac{1}{2}$ of the squares.

(c)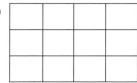

Shade $\frac{1}{3}$ of the squares.

E

What fraction of each diagram is: (a) shaded (b) unshaded?

1 **2** **3** **4** **5**

6 **7** **8** 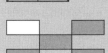 **9** **10**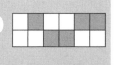

11 What fractions are shown on each of the number lines?

a

0 ⬇ 1

b   c

0 ⬇   ⬇ 1

d   e

0   ⬇   ⬇ 1

12 Copy this grid and shade $\frac{3}{5}$ of the squares.

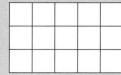

28

M

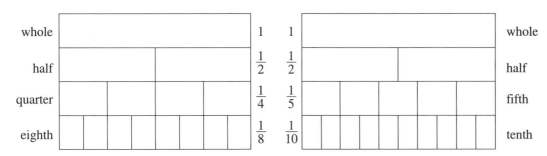

Use the fraction charts to copy and complete by filling in each box below.

1 $\frac{1}{4} = \frac{2}{\square}$ **2** $\frac{1}{2} = \frac{\square}{8}$ **3** $\frac{2}{5} = \frac{\square}{10}$ **4** $\frac{1}{2} = \frac{5}{\square}$

5 $\frac{4}{5} = \frac{\square}{10}$ **6** $1 = \frac{4}{\square}$ **7** $\frac{3}{4} = \frac{\square}{8}$ **8** $1 = \frac{\square}{5}$

9 $1 = \frac{8}{\square}$ **10** $\frac{8}{\square} = \frac{4}{5}$ **11** $\frac{\square}{10} = \frac{1}{5}$ **12** $\frac{\square}{4} = \frac{1}{2}$

13 Which fraction is the odd one out? $\frac{6}{10} \quad \frac{3}{4} \quad \frac{3}{5}$

E

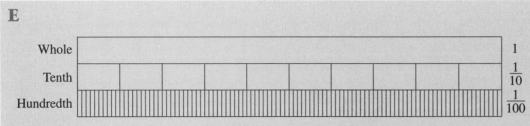

Use the fraction chart to copy and complete by filling in each box below.

1 $\frac{3}{10} = \frac{\square}{100}$ **2** $\frac{20}{100} = \frac{2}{\square}$ **3** $\frac{7}{10} = \frac{\square}{100}$ **4** $\frac{80}{\square} = \frac{8}{10}$

5 $\frac{50}{\square} = \frac{5}{10}$ **6** $\frac{\square}{100} = \frac{6}{10}$ **7** $1 = \frac{\square}{100}$ **8** $\frac{9}{10} = \frac{\square}{100}$

9 Which fraction is the odd one out? $\frac{20}{100} \quad \frac{2}{10} \quad \frac{2}{20}$

10 Which fraction is the odd one out? $\frac{6}{10} \quad \frac{3}{10} \quad \frac{60}{100}$

28

PERCENTAGES ———————————————————

M

1) Answer true or false.

(a) 50% is equal to $\frac{1}{2}$ (b) 28% is more than $\frac{1}{4}$ (c) 70% is more than $\frac{3}{4}$ (d) 75% is equal to $\frac{3}{4}$

2)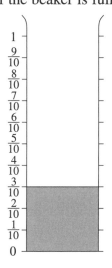

(a) What percentage of the beaker is full?

(b) What percentage of the beaker is full?

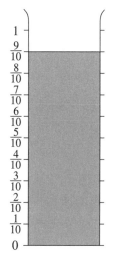

3) Answer true or false.

(a) 40% is equal to $\frac{4}{10}$ (b) $\frac{7}{10}$ is equal to 70%   (c) 35% is more than $\frac{3}{10}$ (d) 82% is more than $\frac{8}{10}$

E

For each shape, write down the shaded area as:

(a) a fraction   (b) a percentage

1)

2)

3)

4)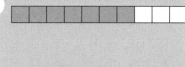

5)

6)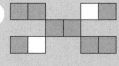

7)

8)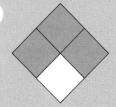

9) Some people were asked if they exercise each week. $\frac{6}{10}$ of the people said they did. What percentage of the people said they did *not*?

10) $\frac{4}{5}$ of people say they like eating fish. What percentage of people do *not* like eating fish?

11) $\frac{3}{4}$ of the children in a school live in the town. What percentage of the children do *not* live in the town?

M

Remember: $25\% = \dfrac{1}{4}$	$50\% = \dfrac{1}{2}$	$75\% = \dfrac{3}{4}$

1 Find 10% of:
- (a) 40
- (b) 50
- (c) 80
- (d) 10
- (e) 200
- (f) 400

2 Find 20% of:
- (a) 40
- (b) 80
- (c) 10
- (d) 200
- (e) 70
- (f) 90

3 Find 60% of:
- (a) 40
- (b) 80
- (c) 30
- (d) 70
- (e) 200
- (f) 60

4 Find 5% of:
- (a) 40
- (b) 80
- (c) 200
- (d) 120
- (e) 600
- (f) 400

5 Find 50% of:
- (a) 16
- (b) 30
- (c) 28
- (d) 32
- (e) 64
- (f) 150

6 Find 25% of:
- (a) 20
- (b) 40
- (c) 12
- (d) 24
- (e) 44
- (f) 100

E

Work out

1 50% of £14

2 10% of 30p

3 5% of 80p

4 25% of £16

5 20% of 50p

6 20% of £180

Find the sale price for each item below.

7
shoes £48
SALE
25% off

8
laptop £600
SALE
5% off

9
dvd player £120
SALE
75% off

10
dishwasher £440
SALE
20% off

11
coat £90
SALE
30% off

12
TV £720
SALE
10% off

13
computer £640
SALE
20% off

14
phone £130
SALE
50% off

15
radio £70
SALE
40% off

DECIMAL FRACTIONS ──────────────────────────── **Main Book page 58**

M

What part of each shape is shaded? Write your answer as a fraction and as a decimal fraction.

1   **2** 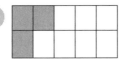   **3**   **4**   **5**

6 Example: 0.9<u>3</u> the underlined 9 is $\dfrac{9}{10}$

Give the value of the underlined figure in each of these numbers.

(a) 3.<u>6</u>   (b) 4.<u>8</u>   (c) <u>7</u>.3   (d) <u>1</u>2.8   (e) 5.<u>3</u>7

(f) <u>9</u>.49   (g) <u>1</u>8.4   (h) 7.<u>9</u>6   (i) 10<u>4</u>.6   (j) 26.<u>3</u>5

7 Write the fraction and decimal fraction shown by each arrow below.

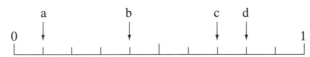

E

> Remember: $0.01 = \dfrac{1}{100}$

Give the value of the underlined figure in each of these numbers.

1 0.<u>8</u>   **2** <u>5</u>.36   **3** 4.8<u>5</u>   **4** 1<u>2</u>.6   **5** 19.<u>8</u>

6 6.1<u>2</u>   **7** 3.6<u>7</u>   **8** <u>1</u>4.16   **9** 17.<u>3</u>8   **10** 15.0<u>3</u>

11 15.<u>2</u>3   **12** 1<u>2</u>3.47   **13** <u>1</u>58.4   **14** 236.<u>5</u>4   **15** 312.4<u>9</u>

16 Write the next 3 terms in each sequence.

(a) 2.5   2.3   2.1   ☐   ☐   ☐

(b) 1.1   1.3   1.5   1.7   ☐   ☐   ☐

17 Work out

(a) 1.8 + 0.6   (b) 0.9 + 2.6   (c) 3.4 − 0.7   (d) 2.3 − 0.6

(e) 3.3 − 2.6   (f) 3.1 − 0.4   (g) 2.7 + 2.4   (h) 1.8 + 1.6

(i) 1.7 + 2.8   (j) 4.3 − 2.4   (k) 3.2 − 2.7   (l) 4.6 + 2.5

M

1 Copy the line. Put each number from the box on the number line.

0 ⌊_____⌋ 1 | 0.1   0.8   0.3   0.6 |

2 Write the smaller of these pairs of numbers.

(a) 1.6   0.6   (b) 3.0   1.3   (c) 1.7   7   (d) 2.4   4.2   (e) 4   0.4   (f) 4.7   7.4

3 Write true or false.

(a) 0.9 is greater than 7   (b) 1.9 is less than 2   (c) 2.5 is less than 3.2   (d) 5 is more than 0.6

4 Put these decimals in order. Start with the smallest number.

(a) 5.2   3.8   2.4   6.1   (b) 3.6   36   6   6.3   (c) 62   6.2   2.6   26

(d) 4.8   4.4   8.4   8.8   (e) 9.7   7   9   7.9   (f) 2.8   2   2.2   8.2

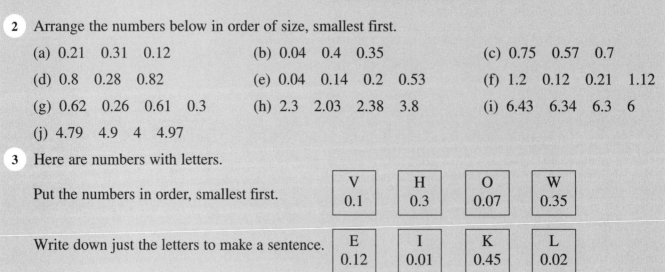

E

1 Copy the line. Put each number from the box on the number line.

1.9   2   2.1 | 1.94   2.03   2.0   2.07   1.98 |
⌊_____⌋

2 Arrange the numbers below in order of size, smallest first.

(a) 0.21   0.31   0.12   (b) 0.04   0.4   0.35   (c) 0.75   0.57   0.7

(d) 0.8   0.28   0.82   (e) 0.04   0.14   0.2   0.53   (f) 1.2   0.12   0.21   1.12

(g) 0.62   0.26   0.61   0.3   (h) 2.3   2.03   2.38   3.8   (i) 6.43   6.34   6.3   6

(j) 4.79   4.9   4   4.97

3 Here are numbers with letters.

Put the numbers in order, smallest first.

V	H	O	W
0.1	0.3	0.07	0.35

Write down just the letters to make a sentence.

E	I	K	L
0.12	0.01	0.45	0.02

M

1 Find one half of:

(a) 18   (b) 40   (c) 28   (d) 38   (e) 62   (f) 36

2 Find one quarter of:

(a) £12   (b) £80   (c) £16   (d) £32   (e) £100   (f) £44

3 Find one tenth of:

(a) 30 cm   (b) 80 cm   (c) 60 cm   (d) 90 cm   (e) 200 cm   (f) 500 cm

4 Tom has £50. He spends one tenth of his money on a book. How much money does he still have?

5 Sita has 36 grapes. She eats one quarter of them. How many grapes does she have left?

E

Work out

1 $\frac{1}{2}$ of 72   **2** $\frac{1}{5}$ of 35   **3** $\frac{1}{3}$ of 12   **4** $\frac{1}{4}$ of 64

5 $\frac{1}{8}$ of 24   **6** $\frac{1}{6}$ of 30   **7** $\frac{1}{5}$ of 40   **8** $\frac{1}{3}$ of 21

9 $\frac{1}{9}$ of 36   **10** $\frac{1}{100}$ of 300   **11** $\frac{1}{100}$ of 600   **12** $\frac{1}{6}$ of 48

13 $\frac{1}{10}$ of 80   **14** $\frac{1}{7}$ of 56   **15** $\frac{1}{100}$ of 900   **16** $\frac{1}{100}$ of 2000

17 $\frac{1}{6}$ of these fish end up inside a whale.

How many of these fish end up inside a whale?

18 Mark has 42 Warhammer pieces. He gives $\frac{1}{7}$ of these pieces to Ann. How many pieces does Mark give to Ann?

19 Change the pounds into pence then find $\frac{1}{100}$ of the following amounts of money.

(a) £5   (b) £9   (c) £6   (d) £20   (e) £45

M

Remember: $49\% = \dfrac{49}{100} = 0.49$ $0.63 = \dfrac{63}{100} = 63\%$

1 Change these percentages into fractions:

(a) 7%   (b) 19%   (c) 20%   (d) 40%   (e) 50%   (f) 13%

2 Change these fractions into percentages.

(a) $\dfrac{3}{100}$ (b) $\dfrac{9}{100}$ (c) $\dfrac{1}{2}$ (d) $\dfrac{31}{100}$ (e) $\dfrac{7}{10}$ (f) $\dfrac{3}{4}$

3 Change these percentages into decimals.

(a) 3%   (b) 30%   (c) 6%   (d) 75%   (e) 70%   (f) 43%

4 Change these decimals into percentages.

(a) 0.08   (b) 0.32   (c) 0.19   (d) 0.04   (e) 0.4   (f) 0.8

5 Change these decimals into fractions.

(a) 0.2   (b) 0.07   (c) 0.23   (d) 0.5   (e) 0.25   (f) 0.87

E

1 (a) Find 10% of £30   (b) Find 30% of £30   (c) Find 40% of £30

2 (a) Find 10% of £80   (b) Find 5% of £80   (c) Find 15% of £80

3 Copy and complete this table.

fraction	$\dfrac{1}{100}$					$\dfrac{27}{100}$
decimal				0.93	0.4	
percentage		17%	25%			

4 (a) Find $\dfrac{1}{3}$ of £27   (b) Find $\dfrac{1}{8}$ of £40   (c) Find $\dfrac{1}{4}$ of £28

5 Jim does 72% of the washing up. What percentage of the washing up still has to be done?

6 Brenda paints $\dfrac{7}{10}$ of her kitchen. What percentage of her kitchen still has to be painted?

7 One quarter of Colin's pets are dogs and 50% are cats. The rest of his pets are rabbits. What percentage of his pets are rabbits?

IMPROPER FRACTIONS 1 ——————————————— **Main Book page 64**

M

> Remember: $\dfrac{11}{3} = 11 \div 3 = 3\dfrac{2}{3}$ $\qquad 2\dfrac{2}{5} = \dfrac{12}{5}$
>
> $\qquad$ improper $\qquad$ mixed
> $\qquad$ fraction $\qquad$ number

Write the shaded areas as both mixed numbers and improper fractions.

1

2

3

4

5

6

7

8

9

Copy and complete.

10 $1\dfrac{1}{2} = \dfrac{\square}{2}$

11 $2\dfrac{4}{5} = \dfrac{\square}{5}$

12 $4\dfrac{3}{4} = \dfrac{\square}{4}$

13 $2\dfrac{2}{3} = \dfrac{8}{\square}$

14 $3\dfrac{1}{3} = \dfrac{\square}{\square}$

15 $\dfrac{13}{5} = 2\dfrac{\square}{5}$

16 $\dfrac{9}{2} = \square\dfrac{\square}{2}$

17 $\dfrac{19}{5} = \square\dfrac{\square}{5}$

18 $\dfrac{7}{4} = \square\dfrac{3}{\square}$

19 $\dfrac{13}{6} = \square\dfrac{\square}{\square}$

E

Change to mixed numbers.

1 $\dfrac{28}{3}$

2 $\dfrac{32}{5}$

3 $\dfrac{19}{2}$

4 $\dfrac{27}{8}$

5 $\dfrac{36}{7}$

6 $\dfrac{38}{5}$

7 $\dfrac{41}{8}$

8 $\dfrac{38}{9}$

9 $\dfrac{44}{7}$

10 $\dfrac{53}{10}$

Change to improper fractions.

11 $4\dfrac{3}{7}$

12 $10\dfrac{3}{4}$

13 $5\dfrac{2}{9}$

14 $4\dfrac{7}{8}$

15 $11\dfrac{1}{5}$

16 $9\dfrac{2}{3}$

17 $10\dfrac{5}{6}$

18 $6\dfrac{1}{9}$

19 $7\dfrac{1}{10}$

20 $7\dfrac{5}{9}$

21 Which is larger? $\left(\dfrac{28}{9} \quad \text{or} \quad \dfrac{16}{3}\right)$

22 Which is larger? $\left(\dfrac{15}{2} \quad \text{or} \quad \dfrac{33}{5}\right)$

Remember: $7n + 3n = 10n$ $7n - n = 6n$ $7n + 4$ cannot be simplified

M

Collect like terms where possible.

1. $4n + 2n$
2. $3a + 5a$
3. $4m + 4m$
4. $8b - 5b$
5. $6y - 2y$
6. $8p - 6p$
7. $4a + a$
8. $7n + n$
9. $7q - q$
10. $5m + 3$
11. $4y - 2$
12. $3x + 4y$
13. $4a + a$
14. $7b + 3c$
15. $3n + 5$
16. $9x - 4x$
17. $7n - 3$
18. $6p + 5p$
19. $9 + 2q$
20. $4m - m$
21. $6x + 4y$
22. $7a + 3a$
23. $5n - n$
24. $8y - 3n$

E

Collect like terms as much as possible.

1. $5n + 3p + 2n + 3p$
2. $4a + 6b + 3a + 2b$
3. $4p + 3p + 5q + 4q$
4. $6m + 4q + 3m + q$
5. $6y + 3w + 2w + 3y$
6. $8n + 4p - 6n - 2p$
7. $9c + 6d - 4c + 3d$
8. $7m + 8q - 3m - 4q$
9. $5a + 4a + 7b - b$
10. $6m + 4 + m + 5$
11. $10p + 9 - p - 6$
12. $8n + 9 - 3n + 4$
13. $8a + 5b + 4c - b + 3c$
14. $6m + 9p + 3m - 7p + 3$
15. $7y + 3y + 9w - y + 5w + 2y$
16. $8a + 6b - 4a + 7b + b - a$
17. $6x + 12y - 3x + y + 3y - x$
18. $9m + 5m + 2p + 3 + 3p - m$
19. $8c + 9d + 14c - 3d + 2c + 4d$
20. $3a + 2 + a + 5b - 3b + 6a + b$

M

Find the perimeter of these shapes if $n = 4$ cm

1

2

3

4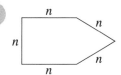

Find the perimeter of these shapes if $a = 7$ cm and $b = 4$ cm

5

6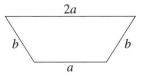

7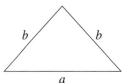

8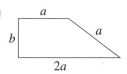

9

10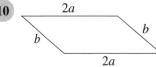

E

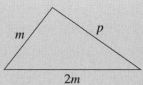

perimeter of triangle $= m + p + 2m = 3m + p$

Find the perimeter of each shape, using the letters m, p and w.

1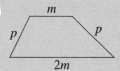

2

3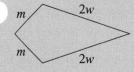

4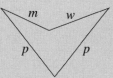

5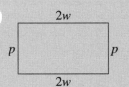

6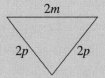

7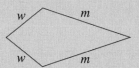

8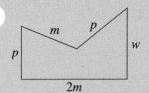

9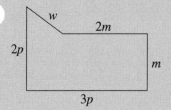

10 For each shape in questions **1** to **9** , find the perimeter if $m = 5$ cm, $p = 3$ cm and $w = 6$ cm.

M

For each of the following triangles state whether it is scalene, isosceles, equilateral or right angled. Lines of the same length are indicated by dashes and equal angles are marked.

1   **2**   **3**   **4**   **5**

6   **7**   **8**   **9**   **10**

E

1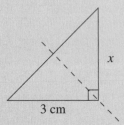

Name this triangle.

How many lines of symmetry does this triangle have?

2 Draw a triangle which has *only* one line of symmetry. What is the special name for this triangle?

3

This right angled triangle has one line of symmetry only.
What is the value of *x*?

3 cm

x

4 What is the name of a triangle with no lines of symmetry and no right angle?

5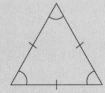

What is the name of each of the four smaller triangles shown in the rectangle?

M

1. Write down the letter at each of the coordinates given below to spell a name.

   (4, 1) (1, 3) (4, 3) (0, 1)

   (5, 1) (1, 2) (3, 0) (2, 4)

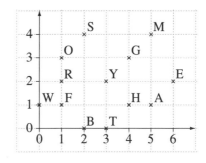

2.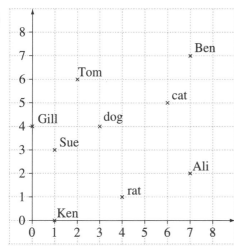

   Write down the co-ordinates of:

   (a) Tom   (b) Ken   (c) Ali

   (d) Gill   (e) Ben   (f) Sue

   Which animal is at

   (g) (4, 1)   (h) (6, 5)   (i) (3, 4)?

E

1.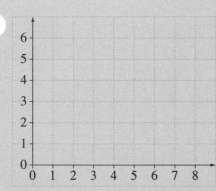

   (a) On squared paper draw the axes shown. Plot the points below and join them up in order.

   (b) (3, 3), (1, 3), (0, 4), (3, 5), (4, 6), (6, 6), (7, 4), (7, 3), (8, 2), (5, 1), (4, 2), (1, 3)

   (c) (5, 5), (5, 4), (6, 2), (7, 3)

   (d) Draw a ● at $(3\frac{1}{2}, 4\frac{1}{2})$

   Now colour in the picture.

2. Draw axes with values from 0 to 10.

   Plot the points below and join them up in order.

   (a) (3, 2), (4, 2), (5, 3), (3, 5), (3, 6), (2, 7), (1, 6), (1, 8), (2, 9), (3, 9), (5, 7), (4, 6), (4, 5), (6, 4), (8, 4), (8, 5), (6, 7), (5, 7)

   (b) (7, 4), (9, 2), (8, 1), (7, 3), (5, 3)

   (c) (1, 6), (2, 8), (2, 9), (2, 7)

   (d) Draw a dot at (3, 8)   Now colour in the picture.

Remember: acute angles are less than 90°

obtuse angles are between 90° and 180°

reflex angles are greater than 180°

M

State whether the angle in each question is acute, obtuse, reflex or a right angle.

11 130°	**12** 40°	**13** 173°	**14** 220°	**15** 305°
16 17°	**17** 263°	**18** 89°	**19** 326°	**20** 90°

E

State whether these angles are correctly or incorrectly labelled. Do *not* measure the angles. Estimate! Where the angles are clearly incorrect, write down an estimate for the correct angle.

1 45°　　**2** 90°　　**3** 120°　　**4** 95°

5 100°　　**6** 300°　　**7** 100°　　**8** 152°

9 120°　　**10** 270°　　**11** 120°　　**12** 240°

13 　　**14** 290°　　**15** 162°　　**16** 85°

M/E

1

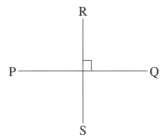

Answer true or false.

'PQ is perpendicular to RS'

2

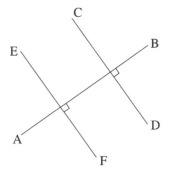

Answer true or false.

'CD is perpendicular to EF'

3 (a) Write down the names of all the sides which are parallel to AB.

(b) Write down the names of all the sides which are parallel to AF.

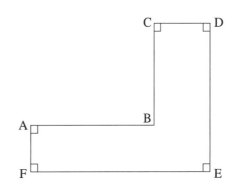

4

(a) How many parallel lines does this letter have?

(b) How many perpendicular lines does this letter have?

5

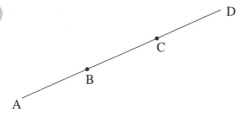

Copy this diagram.

(a) Draw a line through B which is perpendicular to AD.

(b) Draw a line through C which is parallel to the line you have just drawn.

(c) Is your last line parallel or perpendicular to AD?

6 Name an object in your room which has at least two parallel sides.

7 Draw any design of your own which has at least two parallel lines and two perpendicular lines. If possible, show the parallel lines in one colour and the perpendicular lines in a different colour.

UNIT 3

M

Copy and complete.

1 ☐ × 6 = 18   **2** ☐ × 6 = 30   **3** ☐ × 6 = 24   **4** ☐ × 6 = 54

5 ☐ × 6 = 12   **6** ☐ × 6 = 36   **7** ☐ × 6 = 48   **8** ☐ × 6 = 42

9

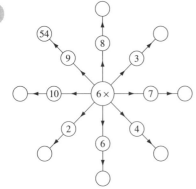

10 ☐ ÷ 6 = 4   **11** ☐ ÷ 6 = 7   **12** ☐ ÷ 6 = 2   **13** ☐ ÷ 6 = 5

14 ☐ ÷ 6 = 3   **15** ☐ ÷ 6 = 1   **16** ☐ ÷ 6 = 10   **17** ☐ ÷ 6 = 6

18 ☐ ÷ 6 = 8   **19** ☐ ÷ 6 = 9   **20** ☐ ÷ 6 = 20   **21** ☐ ÷ 6 = 100

E

Copy and complete.

1 ☐ × 9 = 45   **2** ☐ × 9 = 18   **3** ☐ × 9 = 81   **4** ☐ × 9 = 36

5 ☐ × 9 = 27   **6** ☐ × 9 = 63   **7** ☐ × 9 = 54   **8** ☐ × 9 = 72

9

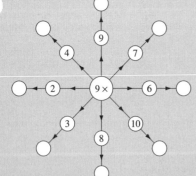

10 ☐ ÷ 9 = 5   **11** ☐ ÷ 9 = 3   **12** ☐ ÷ 9 = 1   **13** ☐ ÷ 9 = 10

14 ☐ ÷ 9 = 2   **15** ☐ ÷ 9 = 8   **16** ☐ ÷ 9 = 4   **17** ☐ ÷ 9 = 6

18 ☐ ÷ 9 = 7   **19** ☐ ÷ 9 = 9   **20** ☐ ÷ 9 = 11   **21** ☐ ÷ 9 = 20

MULTIPLICATION FACTS FOR 7 AND 8 ————————————

M

Copy and complete.

1 ☐ × 7 = 21   **2** ☐ × 7 = 35   **3** ☐ × 7 = 14   **4** ☐ × 7 = 49

5 ☐ × 7 = 56   **6** ☐ × 7 = 28   **7** ☐ × 7 = 42   **8** ☐ × 7 = 63

9

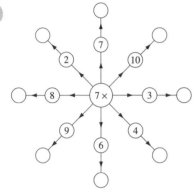

10 ☐ ÷ 7 = 5   **11** ☐ ÷ 7 = 1   **12** ☐ ÷ 7 = 4   **13** ☐ ÷ 7 = 2

14 ☐ ÷ 7 = 7   **15** ☐ ÷ 7 = 3   **16** ☐ ÷ 7 = 6   **17** ☐ ÷ 7 = 10

18 ☐ ÷ 7 = 9   **19** ☐ ÷ 7 = 8   **20** ☐ ÷ 7 = 11   **21** ☐ ÷ 7 = 20

E

Copy and complete.

1 ☐ × 8 = 32   **2** ☐ × 8 = 16   **3** ☐ × 8 = 64   **4** ☐ × 8 = 40

5 ☐ × 8 = 56   **6** ☐ × 8 = 72   **7** ☐ × 8 = 24   **8** ☐ × 8 = 48

9

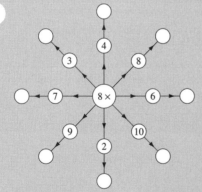

10 ☐ ÷ 8 = 6   **11** ☐ ÷ 8 = 2   **12** ☐ ÷ 8 = 3   **13** ☐ ÷ 8 = 5

14 ☐ ÷ 8 = 1   **15** ☐ ÷ 8 = 4   **16** ☐ ÷ 8 = 10   **17** ☐ ÷ 8 = 7

18 ☐ ÷ 8 = 8   **19** ☐ ÷ 8 = 9   **20** ☐ ÷ 8 = 11   **21** ☐ ÷ 8 = 20

M

Use the rule to write the next 5 numbers each time.

	Start number	Rule
1	632	add 10
2	303	subtract 1
3	674	subtract 10
4	2165	add 100
5	3412	add 1000
6	1986	subtract 100
7	3867	subtract 100
8	2684	add 1000

9 Add 100 to: (a) 3215   (b) 4834   (c) 6523   (d) 5718

10 Take 10 from: (a) 843   (b) 609   (c) 532   (d) 654

11 Add 1000 to: (a) 6814   (b) 3972   (c) 4083   (d) 2419

E

Copy and complete the calculation squares.

1

+	10	100	1	1000
598	608			
2146				
3167				
5258				

2

−	1	100	10	1000
1784	1783			
2819				
4328				
6523				

3 Add 20 to: (a) 648   (b) 837   (c) 2146   (d) 5218

4 Add 300 to: (a) 1682   (b) 473   (c) 3240   (d) 6375

5 Take 30 from: (a) 452   (b) 2194   (c) 311   (d) 3062

6 Take 200 from: (a) 3164   (b) 2849   (c) 4003   (d) 2614

ORDERING NUMBERS ────────────────────────────

Remember: > 'is greater than'   < 'is less than'

M

Write down the number that is halfway on each of these number lines.

(1) 300 _____ 400

(2) 320 _____ 330

(3) 180 _____ 190

(4) 350 _____ 450

(5) 3000 _____ 3100

(6) 1240 _____ 1260

(7) Put these numbers in order starting with the smallest.

(a) 215 512 152 352

(b) 607 670 476 467

(c) 1368 1863 1516 1637

(d) 4160 4127 4235 4194

(8) Answer 'true' or 'false'

(a) $36 > 63$ (b) $402 < 420$ (c) $3 \times 10 > 4 \times 8$ (d) $5 \times 5 < 3 \times 8$

(9) Copy and complete by putting <, > or = in the box.

(a) $6 \times 2 \ \square \ 3 \times 3$

(b) $8 \times 5 \ \square \ 4 \times 10$

(c) $4 \times 2 \ \square \ 5 \times 3$

(d) $2 \times 10 \ \square \ 4 \times 6$

(e) $3 \times 2 \ \square \ 2 \times 3$

(f) $4 \times 9 \ \square \ 3 \times 10$

(g) $2 \times 5 \ \square \ 3 \times 6$

(h) $4 \times 5 \ \square \ 5 \times 5$

(i) $8 \times 2 \ \square \ 4 \times 4$

E

Write down the number that is halfway between each pair of numbers.

(1) 1000 ←→ 1500

(2) 750 ←→ 850

(3) 2170 ←→ 2370

(4) 5120 ←— 5220

(5) 1320 ←→ 1400

(6) 3450 ←→ 3530

(7) Answer 'true' or 'false'

(a) $7 \times 7 < 8 \times 6$

(b) $9 \times 7 > 8 \times 8$

(c) $6 \times 8 > 7 \times 6$

(8) Copy and complete by putting <, > or = in the box.

(a) $7 \times 5 \ \square \ 6 \times 6$

(b) $9 \times 8 \ \square \ 7 \times 11$

(c) $8 \times 10 \ \square \ 9 \times 9$

(d) $6 \times 9 \ \square \ 8 \times 7$

(e) $6 \times 10 \ \square \ 4 \times 15$

(f) $7 \times 9 \ \square \ 2 \times 34$

(g) $6 \times 8 \ \square \ 3 \times 14$

(h) $9 \times 8 \ \square \ 5 \times 14$

(I) $6 \times 7 \ \square \ 2 \times 21$

(j) $7 \times 7 \ \square \ 3 \times 15$

(k) $7 \times 8 \ \square \ 12 \times 5$

(l) $6 \times 15 \ \square \ 8 \times 12$

M

Copy the grids and put a ring around all the multiples of the number shown.

1 Multiples of 4.

1	2	3	4	5	6
7	8	9	10	11	12
13	14	15	16	17	18
19	20	21	22	23	24
25	26	27	28	29	30

2 Multiples of 6.

		3	6		
	9	12	15	18	
21	24	27	30	33	36
39	42	45	48	51	54
	57	60	63	66	
	69	72			

3 Multiples of 8.

4	8	12	16	20	24
					28
52	48	44	40	36	32
56					
60	64	68	72	76	80

4 Multiples of 9.

6						
12	18	24	30	36		78
84				42		72
90	96	102		48	54	60	66

E

1 Write down the first six multiples of 5.

2 Write down the first six multiples of 7.

3 Which of these numbers are multiples of 3?

> 9   13   8   36
> 25   60   47   45

4 Which of these numbers are *not* multiples of 11?

> 44   77   30   22
> 110   28   55   99

5 15   30   45 … write down the next five multiples of 15.

6 23   46   69 … write down the next five multiples of 23.

M

1 Draw a different rectangle using 6 small squares.

2 Draw two different rectangles using 10 small squares.

3 Draw all the different rectangles you can make from

(a) 14 small squares   (b) 15 small squares   (c) 18 small squares

4 In question **3** you should have drawn two different rectangles from 14 small squares (length 14, width 1 and length 7, width 2). We say the factors of 14 are 14, 1, 7 and 2.

(a) Look at your question **3** rectangles with 15 small squares and write down the factors of 15.

(b) Look at your question **3** rectangles with 18 small squares and write down the factors of 18.

E

Example: the factors of 8 are 1 and 8, 2 and 4 (2 pairs of factors)

Find all the pairs of factors of the following:

1 22 (there are 2 pairs)   **2** 12 (there are 3 pairs)

3 4 (there are 2 pairs)   **4** 26 (there are 2 pairs)

5 20   **6** 30   **7** 44   **8** 50

9 24   **10** 55   **11** 32   **12** 7

PRIME NUMBERS 2 ——————————————————————— **Main Book page 90**

M

1 Write down the prime number in each group.

    (a) 10, 11, 12   (b) 13, 14, 15   (c) 19, 20, 21

    (d) 27, 28, 29   (e) 31, 32, 33   (f) 36, 37, 38

2 Write down all the prime numbers shown opposite.

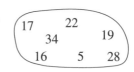

3 Write down all the prime numbers between 40 and 50.

E

1 Write down the next prime number after:

    (a) 20   (b) 50   (c) 65   (d) 85

2 Write down all the prime numbers between 50 and 100.

SHORT MULTIPLICATION ——————————————————— **Main Book page 91**

M

Work out

1   63
  × 4

2   34
  × 5

3   31
  × 4

4   42
  × 3

5   64
  × 6

6   48
  × 7

7   27
  × 4

8   36
  × 6

9   47
  × 9

10   53
  × 5

11   84
  × 6

12   79
  × 8

13   54
  × 7

14   68
  × 5

15   29
  × 9

E

Work out

1   423
  × 5

2   385
  × 4

3   472
  × 6

4   218
  × 3

5   576
  × 8

6 436 × 9   7 274 × 6   8 187 × 5   9 366 × 4   10 268 × 7

11 764 × 5   12 348 × 8   13 809 × 7   14 435 × 3   15 493 × 9

16 224 children each give £6 to a charity. How much money do they give in total?

M

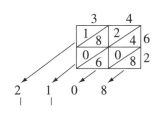

Use the grid method or any other way you wish to use to work out the questions below.

1 26 × 32   **2** 41 × 15   **3** 23 × 34   **4** 14 × 33

5 12 × 45   **6** 24 × 31   **7** 35 × 13   **8** 22 × 42

9 Tom earns £23 each Saturday. How much does he earn in 12 Saturdays?

E

Work out

1 26 × 32   **2** 35 × 26   **3** 53 × 46   **4** 62 × 37

5 28 × 67   **6** 43 × 84   **7** 47 × 78   **8** 94 × 53

9

Paint cost per pot	
5 litres pink	£12
5 litres blue	£13
10 litres red	£21
10 litres yellow	£23

(a) Marie buys 15 pots of red paint. How much does this cost?

(b) Danny is a decorator. He buys 24 pots of blue paint and 29 pots of yellow paint. How much does this cost in total?

REMAINDERS ———————————————————

Example: $19 \div 4 = 4$ remainder 3

M

Copy and complete.

1 $11 \div 2 = 5$ rem. ☐   **2** $23 \div 3 = 7$ rem. ☐

3 $19 \div 5 = 3$ rem. ☐   **4** $34 \div 5 = 6$ rem. ☐

5 $28 \div 3 = 9$ rem. ☐   **6** $17 \div 4 = 4$ rem. ☐

7 $61 \div 10 = 6$ rem. ☐   **8** $46 \div 10 = 4$ rem. ☐

Work out and give the remainder as a whole number.

9 $26 \div 4$ **10** $33 \div 4$ **11** $52 \div 10$ **12** $29 \div 5$

13 $14 \div 3$ **14** $24 \div 5$ **15** $20 \div 3$ **16** $32 \div 10$

17 Seven pieces of cheese are shared between three people. How many pieces does each person get and how many pieces are left over?

E

Work out and give the remainder as a whole number.

1 $482 \div 6$ **2** $715 \div 4$ **3** $895 \div 6$ **4** $164 \div 3$

5 $514 \div 8$ **6** $375 \div 9$ **7** $235 \div 6$ **8** $657 \div 10$

9 $364 \div 9$ **10** $286 \div 7$ **11** $517 \div 8$ **12** $800 \div 7$

13 $473 \div 6$ **14** $815 \div 9$ **15** $647 \div 7$ **16** $529 \div 8$

17 A cinema ticket costs £6. How many tickets can be bought for £132?

18 112 children are split into teams of 7. How many teams are there?

M

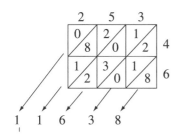

$253 \times 46 = 11638$

Use the grid method or any other way you wish to use to work out the questions below.

1. 134×25
2. 215×32
3. 223×51
4. 412×32

5. 253×14
6. 145×23
7. 304×30
8. 524×24

9. A bus travels 143 miles each day. How far does the bus travel in 14 days?

E

Use any method to work out the questions below.

1. 317×26
2. 227×43
3. 526×54
4. 718×46

5. 436×74
6. 825×64
7. 237×182
8. 649×328

9. Carla earns £23 per hour. One month she works for 152 hours. Ben earns £21 per hour. During the month he works 5 days each week for 4 weeks. On each day he works for 8 hours. Who earns the most money during this month and by how much?

10. A party of 347 people travel to the Olympic Games. Each person pays £78. How much money do these people pay in total?

SHORT DIVISION

Examples:

$$3\overline{)97^12} = 324$$

$4 \div 5$ is the same as $4.0 \div 5$

$$5\overline{)4.^40} = 0.8$$

M

Work out

1 $5\overline{)35}$ **2** $4\overline{)24}$ **3** $6\overline{)30}$ **4** $2\overline{)104}$ **5** $3\overline{)13.2}$ **6** $2\overline{)16.8}$

7 $5\overline{)17.5}$ **8** $3\overline{)28.2}$ **9** $4\overline{)13.6}$ **10** $6\overline{)13.8}$ **11** $6\overline{)32.4}$ **12** $5\overline{)28.5}$

Give these answers in pounds, for example: £4.80.

13 £12.60 ÷ 4   **14** £13.80 ÷ 3   **15** £11.35 ÷ 5   **16** £8.46 ÷ 3

17 £14.34 ÷ 6   **18** £19 ÷ 5   **19** £26 ÷ 5   **20** £15.40 ÷ 7

E

Work out

1 $4\overline{)856}$ **2** $5\overline{)1630}$ **3** $8\overline{)1264}$ **4** $6\overline{)3942}$ **5** $9\overline{)324}$

6 $6\overline{)2766}$ **7** $7\overline{)3759}$ **8** $9\overline{)1971}$ **9** $2\overline{)2.3}$ **10** $3\overline{)14.16}$

11 $4\overline{)13.8}$ **12** $5\overline{)43}$ **13** $2\overline{)9.9}$ **14** $5\overline{)14}$ **15** $8\overline{)49.2}$

16 Six people win £394.80 in a talent show.
The money is shared equally. How much
does each person get?

17 A bill of £82 is shared equally by five people.
How much does each person pay?

ROUNDING REMAINDERS UP OR DOWN 1 ──────────────── **Main Book page 96**

In these questions, think carefully about whether you should round *up* or *down*.

M

1 A taxi can carry 5 people. How many taxis are needed to carry 32 people?

2 A cinema ticket costs £6. How many tickets can be bought for £50?

3 Hal saves £3 every week. How long will it take him to save £17?

4 A car can carry 4 children as passengers. How many cars are needed to carry 43 children?

5 There are 29 children in a class. How many teams of 5 can be made?

6 93 chocolates are to be packed into bags of 10. How many full bags can be made?

E

1 An egg box holds 6 eggs. How many boxes do you need for 304 eggs?

2 How many 7 pence chews can I buy with £2?

3 9 children can sleep in a large tent. How many tents are needed for 110 children?

4

Models	
£8	Thunderbird 1
£7	Thunderbird 2
£4	Thunderbird 4

(a) How many Thunderbird 1 models can I buy with £150?

(b) How many Thunderbird 2 models can I buy with £212?

5 Pencils are packed into boxes of 8. How many boxes are filled completely if you have 573 pencils?

6 How many 6 cm pieces of wood can be cut from a 2 metre piece of wood?

7 A charity puts £3 into each Christmas gift box. How many gift boxes can be done in this way if the charity has £6500?

ROUNDING ————————————————————————————

M

1 Round to the nearest 10.

(a) 18   (b) 32   (c) 41   (d) 75   (e) 36   (f) 55

2 Round to the nearest 100.

(a) 340   (b) 560   (c) 270   (d) 352   (e) 436   (f) 745

3 Round to the nearest 10.

(a) 278   (b) 363   (c) 512   (d) 328   (e) 106   (f) 672

4 Write down which numbers round off to 600 (to the nearest 100).

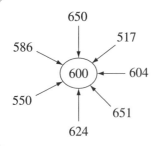

5 Answer 'true' or 'false'

(a) 38 is 40 to the nearest 10   (b) 529 is 520 to the nearest 10

(c) 462 is 500 to the nearest 100   (d) 354 is 300 to the nearest 100

E

1 Round to the nearest whole number.

(a) 6.4   (b) 4.5   (c) 7.6   (d) 16.2   (e) 3.16   (f) 4.64

2 Round to the nearest metre.

(a) 7. 8 m   (b) 3.9 m   (c) 2.4 m   (d) 4.7 m   (e) 0.63 m   (f) 6.12 m

3 Write down which numbers round off to £8 (to the nearest pound).

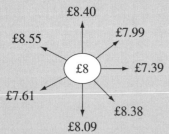

4 Round to the nearest kilogram.

(a) 7.3 kg   (b) 1.9 kg   (c) 4.2 kg   (d) 2.16 kg   (e) 5.68 kg   (f) 7.31 kg

5 Answer 'true' or 'false'

(a) 9.6 m is 10 m to the nearest metre   (b) £4.48 is £5 to the nearest pound

(c) 7.18 kg is 7 kg to the nearest kg   (d) £13.50 is £14 to the nearest pound

ORDER OF OPERATIONS ────────────────

Remember: BODMAS – Brackets, Divide, Multiply, Add, Subtract

M

Work out

1 $8 - 3 \times 2$

2 $5 + 4 \times 3$

3 $7 + 4 \times 6$

4 $3 \times 5 + 4$

5 $7 + 12 \div 3$

6 $8 + 16 \div 2$

7 $15 - 9 \div 3$

8 $30 \div 6 + 7$

9 $45 \div 9 - 4$

10 $28 + 4 \times 11$

11 $4 + 2 \times 6$

12 $6 - 4 \times 1$

13 $(4 + 6) \times 2$

14 $20 - (2 + 3)$

15 $5 \times (10 - 1)$

16 $5 \times 3 + 2 \times 4$

17 $6 \times 3 - 2 \times 5$

18 $10 \div 5 + 4 \times 4$

19 $20 \div 4 + 8 \div 2$

20 $(6 + 4) \times 3$

21 $(15 + 25) \div (3 + 7)$

E

Work out

1 $3 + 5 \times 7 + 4$

2 $28 - 3 \times 6 + 4$

3 $5 + 20 \div 5 + 3$

4 $12 - 30 \div 6 - 2$

5 $27 \div 9 + 3 \times 6$

6 $42 \div 7 - 36 \div 6$

7 $48 - 6 \times 7 + 9$

8 $8 \times 9 \div 3 + 7$

9 $7 \times 9 - 54 \div 9$

10 $(8 - 2) \times 8$

11 $56 \div (9 - 2)$

12 $(6 + 4) \times (15 - 8)$

13 $(13 + 11) \div (12 - 6)$

14 $9 \times (24 - 15)$

15 $5 \times 9 - 4 \times 7$

16 $72 \div 8 + 3 \times 7$

17 $(14 + 6) \times (7 - 4)$

18 $17 + 49 \div 7 - 16$

19 Copy and fill in each box to give the correct answer

(a) $5 \times \square + 2 = 22$

(b) $\square \times 7 - 6 = 15$

(c) $6 + 10 \div \square = 8$

(d) $\square + 3 \times 8 = 29$

(e) $(8 - \square) \times 7 = 28$

(f) $15 \div (1 + \square) = 3$

METRIC UNITS OF MASS AND CAPACITY ────────

Reminder: 1 kg = 1000 g   1 litre = 1000 ml

M

Copy and complete

1 7500 g = ☐ kg ☐ g = 7.5 kg

2 9500 g = ☐ kg ☐ g = ☐ kg

3 3000 g = ☐ kg ☐ g = ☐ kg

4 6000 g = ☐ kg ☐ g = ☐ kg

For each of the scales work out the measurement indicated by each of the arrows.

5
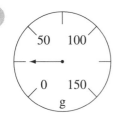

6
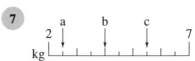

7

8 Answer 'true' or 'false'

   (a) 6500 ml = 6 litres 500 ml = 6.5 litres

   (b) 0.5 litres = 50 ml

   (c) 1500 ml = 1 litre 500 ml = 1.5 litres

   (d) 4.5 litres = 4 litres 500 ml = 4500 ml

E

Write as grams

1 0.8 kg

2 2.4 kg

3 5.2 kg

4 4.9 kg

5 2.6 kg

6 3.7 kg

7 8.8 kg

8 7.3 kg

For each of the scales work out the measurement indicated by each of the arrows.

9
ml
900
a
b
c
500

10
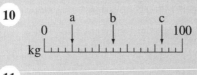

11

12
litres

Write as kilograms

13   6400 g

14 3200 g

15   5700 g

16   3600 g

17   300 g

M

1. Would you expect these things to be longer or shorter then 1 metre?

   (a) a mobile phone   (b) an mp3 player   (c) the height of a woman

2. Would you expect these things to be longer or shorter than 1 centimetre?

   (a) the length of a pen   (b) the width of a pin   (c) the height of an egg cup

3. | millimetre   centimetre   metre   kilometre |

   Which metric unit would you choose to measure the length of:

   (a) a house   (b) an ear stud   (c) a car

   (d) a bar of chocolate   (e) France   (f) a spoon

4. Estimate the height of a door.

5. Estimate the length of your pen.

E

1. Would you expect these things to weigh more or less than 1 kilogram?

   (a) a man   (b) a rubber   (c) a motorbike

2. For each item write down which weight seems more sensible.

   (a) a pear (100 g or 1 kg)   (b) a van (200 g or 2000 kg)

   (c) a bag of sugar (2 g or 2 kg)   (d) a child (25 kg or 2500 kg)

3. Answer 'true' or 'false'

   (a) A can of lemonade contains 330 ml.

   (b) A bucket has a capacity of 80 ml.

   (c) The capacity of a teaspoon is 5 ml.

   (d) A full car petrol tank contains 40 litres.

| MASS PROBLEMS | Main Book page 105 |

Remember: 1 kg = 1000 g

M

1 Charlie weighs 38 kg. His brother weighs 26 kg more. How much does his brother weigh?

2 A cake weighs 1 kg. It is cut into ten equal slices. How much does each slice weigh?

3 John has 1 kg of sugar. He uses 5700 g of sugar in his baking. How much sugar is left?

4 An apple weighs 90 g. What is the weight of 8 apples?

5 A man trips over and gets covered in mud. He weighs himself at 91 kg. He usually weighs 79 kg. What is the weight of the mud?

6 Jasmine has 2 kg of potatoes. She uses 800 g in her cooking. What is the weight of the potatoes that are left?

7 A CD weighs 70 g. What is the weight of 9 CDs?

E

1 One tin of beans weighs 250 g. What do 6 tins weigh? Give your answer in kilograms and grams.

2 Meryl asks for $\frac{1}{4}$ kg of cheese. How many grams does she ask for?

3 Nigel has 4 kg of butter and uses 1400 g during one day. How much butter is left? Give your answer in grams.

4 Copy and complete

| 2500 g = … kg | 5.4 kg = … g | 2.9 kg = … g | 800 g = … kg |

5 A box weighs 4.8 kg. How much do 10 boxes weigh?

6 A packet weighs 450 g. Another packet weighs twice as much. What is the total weight of the two packets. Give your answer in kilograms and grams.

CAPACITY PROBLEMS

Main Book page 106

Remember: 1 litre = 1000 ml

M

1. Denise uses 7 buckets of water to clean her car. Each bucket holds 5 litres. How much water does Denise use?

2. A shandy is made with 300 ml of beer and 250 ml of lemonade. How much shandy is there?

3. A supermarket has 18 litres of yoghurt. 12 litres are sold. How much yoghurt is left?

4. Terry uses a hosepipe to water his garden. He uses 4 litres of water in one minute. How much water does he use in half an hour?

5. Zoe drank 3 cans of coke. Each can contained 180 ml. How much coke did Zoe drink?

6. Five children shared 700 ml of lemon squash. How much lemon squash does each child get?

E

1. 1300 ml is drunk from a 2 litre bottle of lemonade. How much lemonade is left?

2. A large bottle of milk contains 750 ml. How much milk is there in 4 bottles? Give your answer in litres.

3. Donna is letting people have a taster from a bottle of wine. Each bottle contains 750 ml. Each small glass contains 50 ml. How many small glasses can Donna fill from one bottle?

4. Pete adds 2.8 litres of water to 350 ml of floor cleaner. How much mixture is there? Give your answer in litres.

5. Marion throws three and a half litres of water over her car then throws another 850 ml. How much water did she use? Give your answer in litres and millilitres.

6. Copy and complete

| 4500 ml = … litres | 6.2 litres = … ml | 1.8 litres = … ml | 400 ml = … litres |

7. A 1.5 litre bottle of coke fills 10 glasses. How much coke can each glass hold?

UNITS OF TIME |

Remember: 1 year = 365 days	1 day = 24 hours
= 52 weeks	1 hour = 60 minutes
= 12 months	1 minute = 60 seconds

M

Copy and complete

1 2 years = ☐ weeks

2 4 weeks = ☐ days

3 3 days = ☐ hours

4 3 years = ☐ months

5 ☐ minutes = 3 hours

6 ☐ weeks = 14 days

7 $\frac{1}{2}$ hour = ☐ minutes

8 ☐ months = 5 years

9 ☐ hours = 10 days

10 2 years = ☐ days

MARCH						
Su	M	Tu	W	Th	F	Sa
	1	2	3	4	5	6
7	8	9	10	11	12	13
14	15	16	17	18	19	20
21	22	23	24	25	26	27
28	29	30	31			

11 How many Fridays are there in March?

12 How many days are there in March?

13 On which day of the week falls:

(a) March 4th   (b) March 23rd

(c) March 7th   (d) March 20th

14 What is the date of the second Friday in March?

E

Answer 'true' or 'false'

1 8 hours = 48 minutes

2 9 weeks = 63 days

3 48 hours = 2 days

4 84 months = 6 years

5 $1\frac{1}{2}$ days = 36 hours

6 10 years = 32500 days

7 5 years = 260 weeks

8 $3\frac{1}{2}$ minutes = 150 seconds

SEPTEMBER						
Su	M	Tu	W	Th	F	Sa
				1	2	3
4	5	6	7	8	9	10
11	12	13	14	15	16	17
18	19	20	21	22	23	24
25	26	27	28	29	30	

9 Tania goes on holiday from September 12th until September 20th

(a) On which day of the week is the first day of her holiday?

(b) On which day of the week does she come back from holiday?

10 What is the date of the fourth Thursday in September?

READING CLOCKS ────────────────────── **Main Book page 108**

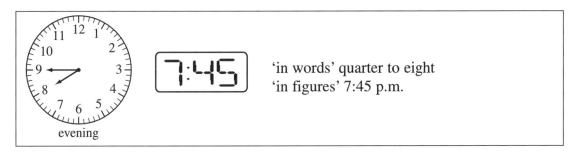

'in words' quarter to eight
'in figures' 7:45 p.m.

M

Write the times shown on these clocks:

(a) in words   (b) in figures, using a.m. and p.m.

1   **2**   **3**   **4**

afternoon   morning   morning   afternoon

5    **6**   **7**   **8**

evening   morning   afternoon   evening

9 What would be the time if each clock in questions **1** to **4** was 5 minutes fast?

10 What would be the time if each clock in questions **5** to **8** was 10 minutes slow?

E

Write the times shown on these clocks:

(a) in words   (b) in figures, using a.m. and p.m.

1    **2**    **3**    **4**

evening   evening   morning   afternoon

5    **6**    **7**     **8**

evening   morning   morning   evening

9 What would be the time if each clock in questions **1** to **4** was 30 minutes fast?

10 What would be the time if each clock in questions **5** to **8** was 14 minutes slow?

M

Use the timetable opposite.

1 Which programme starts at 7:45?

2 How long are the following programmes?

    (a) Home and Away   (b) Emmerdale

    (c) News before 6   (d) The Bill

3 (a) How long was the first part of Indiana Jones?

    (b) How long was the second part of Indiana Jones?

    (c) How long did Indiana Jones last in total?

ITV 3	
5:45	News before 6
6:00	Local news
6:30	Home and Away
7:00	Emmerdale
7:45	The Bill
8:45	Indiana Jones (Film)
10:20	News
10:35	Indiana Jones (Film)
11:30	Local sport

4 The bus journey from the cinema to the supermarket takes 25 minutes. Buses run every 20 minutes. Copy and complete the times on this bus timetable.

	Bus 1	Bus 2	Bus 3	Bus 4	Bus 5	Bus 6	Bus 7
cinema	7:00	7:20					
supermarket	7:25						

5 Which bus would Gethin need to be on if he wants to be at the supermarket by:

(a) 7:30   (b) 9:00   (c) 8:15   (d) 7:50?

E

1 Copy and complete this train timetable. Each train takes the same time between stations.

	Train 1	Train 2	Train 3	Train 4	Train 5	Train 6	Train 7
Catford	9:00	9:50	10:32	11:14	11:43		
Malham	9:08					12:00	
Howsey	9:21		10:53				
Medstow	9:46						
Denton	9:55				12:38		12:59

2 Kapil needs to get to Medstow by 12:15. Which is the latest train he could catch from Catford?

3 Sarah needs to get to Denton by 10:30. Which is the latest train she could catch from Malham?

4 How long does the train take to get from Malham to Medstow?

63

TIME PROBLEMS ———————————————— | Main Book page 112 |

M

1. David left home at 8:15 a.m. It took him 35 minutes to walk to school. At what time did he arrive at school?

2. A rugby game starts at 3:05 p.m. and lasts for 50 minutes. When does the game finish?

3. It takes Julie 25 minutes to walk to the shop. She sets off at 5:15 p.m. When does she arrive?

4. Luke goes swimming at 3:45 p.m. He swims for 40 minutes. When does he finish?

5. Ed goes to the gym at 6:50 p.m. He stays for 35 minutes. When does he leave?

6. Ruby leaves college at 3:40 p.m. It takes her 25 minutes to walk to a café. When does she arrive at the café?

7. A watch shows 11:15. The real time is 10:45. How many minutes fast is the watch?

E

1. A bus leaves the station at 11:23 and arrives at the town centre at 12:05. How long is the journey?

2. A maths lesson starts at 10:20. It lasts for 55 minutes. When does it finish?

3. Copy and complete the finish times for each of these lessons.

lesson	Art	English	Science	PE
start time	09:30	09:10	11:15	10:35
lesson time	45 minutes	55 minutes	45 minutes	1 hour 10 minutes
finish time				

4. A play begins at 2:20 p.m. and finishes at 4:05 p.m. How long is the play?

5. A plane flies from Heathrow at 05:40 and arrives in New York 3 hours 50 minutes later. At what time does it arrive in New York?

6. Meg arrives at the railway station at 08:30. She waits 25 minutes for her train. The train journey takes 46 minutes. It then takes her another 12 minutes to walk to work. When does she arrive at her workplace?

M

1 Maggie has 14 sweets. Jack has 13 more sweets than Maggie. How many sweets do they have altogether?

2 Mark buys a bar of chocolate for 64 p. How much change from £1 does he get?

3 There are 50 people on a bus. 23 people get off and 7 people get on at the station. How many people are now on the bus?

4 There are 66 people in the cinema. Half the people leave but 20 people come in. How many people are in the cinema now?

5 Wes is double the age of Naomi. How old is Naomi if Wes is 34 years old?

6 Sandra takes seven minutes to run one mile. How long will it take Sandra to run six miles?

7 It takes Pete 20 minutes to wash a car. How many cars can he wash in 100 minutes?

E

1 Dom has collected 28 football cards. He needs 3 more cards to have half of the possible cards. How many possible cards are there in total?

2 Marcus usually plays tennis for 75 minutes. He falls over and has to stop playing 28 minutes before the end. How long did he play tennis for?

3 How many days are there in nine weeks?

4 There are 203 children in a school. 14 are absent and 65 go on a school trip. How many children are left in school?

5 A box has 12 pencils in it. A school orders 6 boxes. What is the total number of pencils in these 6 boxes?

6 Mrs Williams shares £48 equally between her six grandchildren. How much does each grandchild get?

MONEY PROBLEMS ────────────────────────── | **Main Book page 114** |

M

1 Change to pence.

(a) £3.40 (b) £4.75 (c) £6.49 (d) £5.42

2 Change to pounds and pence.

(a) 428 p (b) 560 p (c) 728 p (d) 154 p

3 Work out the cost of this food and the change from £5.00.

(a) 1 chips, 2 sausages   (b) 1 fish, 1 chips

(c) 2 chips, 2 burgers   (d) 1 chips, 1 fishcake

(e) 3 pies, 2 peas   (f) 2 sausages, 2 beans

(g) 2 chips, 1 sausage, 1 peas   (h) 3 chips, 2 fishcakes, 1 peas, 1 beans

chips	90 p
fishcake	55 p
sausage	50 p
peas	45 p
beans	40 p
fish	£2.30
burger	£1.40
pie	£1.25

4 How many fishcakes can you buy for £5.00?

E

1 Change to pence.

(a) £8.64 (b) £3.09 (c) £4.12 (d) £5.07

2 Change to pounds and pence.

(a) 316 p (b) 39 p (c) 74 p (d) 657 p

3

sweets	65 p
crisps	45 p
mints	40 p
gum	35 p
magazine	£1.80
pen	£1.45
calculator	£5.20
glue	£1.65

Work out the cost of these items and the change from £10.00.

(a) 2 magazines

(b) 3 pens

(c) 1 calculator, 1 pen

(d) 2 mints, 1 gum, 1 crisps

(e) 1 gum, 1 sweets, 2 pens

(f) 1 calculator, 1 glue, 1 magazine

(g) 3 pens, 2 glues, 1 crisps

(h) 1 calculator, 2 pens, 1 glue

4 You buy 2 pens, 1 magazine and one other item. You pay with a £10 note and receive £4.65 change. What is the other item?

M/E

1 This bar chart shows how many people in a
hotel came from each different country
(G = Germany, F = France, UK = United Kingdom,
S = Spain, I = Italy)

(a) How many people came from Spain?

(b) How many people came from France?

(c) How many more people came from the
UK than France?

(d) What was the total number of people?

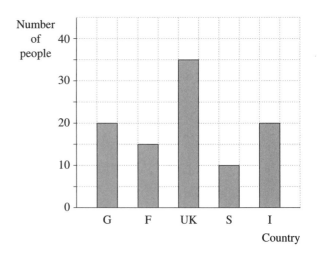

2 Some children were asked how many times they had a drink of water each day.
The replies are listed below:

2	4	3	0	2	4	6	5
5	2	7	1	3	3	2	6
1	3	6	4	5	1	0	3
6	3	4	4	2	5	3	4

(a) Copy and complete the frequency table.

number of times	tally	frequency
0		
1		
2		
3		
4		
5		
6		
7		

(b) Draw a bar chart to show the results.

3 The temperature in a centrally heated house is recorded every hour from 06:00 till 21:00. The results are shown below.

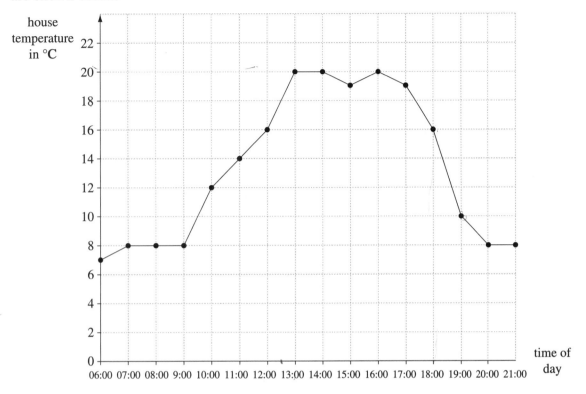

(a) What was the temperature at 16:00 h?

(b) What was the temperature at 10:00 h?

(c) What was the temperature at 12:30 h?

(d) Write down the two times when the temperature was 16°C.

(e) When do you think the central heating was switched on?

(f) Write down the two times when the temperature was 10°C.

(g) When do you think the central heating was switched off?

M

Work out in your head

1 $18 + 16$ **2** $26 + 24$ **3** $45 + 46$ **4** $84 + 85$

5 $32 + 34$ **6** $60 + 50$ **7** $28 + 30$ **8** $90 + 70$

9 $30 + 40$ **10** $44 + 46$ **11** $75 + 77$ **12** $95 + 94$

Work out these in your head as well

13 18×2 **14** 23×2 **15** 340×2 **16** 460×2

17 690×2 **18** 2400×2 **19** $86 \div 2$ **20** $38 \div 2$

21 $320 \div 2$ **22** $4600 \div 2$ **23** $7200 \div 2$ **24** $9600 \div 2$

E

Work out in your head

1 $270 + 270$ **2** $340 + 340$ **3** $180 + 180$ **4** $490 + 490$

5 $260 + 260$ **6** $530 + 530$ **7** $190 + 190$ **8** $380 + 380$

9 $760 + 760$ **10** 68×2 **11** 88×2 **12** 49×2

13 $146 \div 2$ **14** $166 \div 2$ **15** $174 \div 2$

Copy and complete

16 $\boxed{33} \longrightarrow \boxed{\times 2} \longrightarrow \boxed{} \longrightarrow \boxed{\times 2} \longrightarrow \boxed{}$

17 $\boxed{13} \longrightarrow \boxed{\times 2} \longrightarrow \boxed{} \longrightarrow \boxed{\times 2} \longrightarrow \boxed{}$

18 $\boxed{184} \longrightarrow \boxed{\div 2} \longrightarrow \boxed{} \longrightarrow \boxed{\div 2} \longrightarrow \boxed{}$

19 $\boxed{116} \longrightarrow \boxed{\div 2} \longrightarrow \boxed{} \longrightarrow \boxed{\div 2} \longrightarrow \boxed{}$

20 $\boxed{99} \longrightarrow \boxed{\times 2} \longrightarrow \boxed{} \longrightarrow \boxed{\div 2} \longrightarrow \boxed{} \longrightarrow \boxed{\div 2} \longrightarrow \boxed{}$

TRIANGULAR AND SQUARE NUMBERS ——————— Main Book page 122

M

1 Draw one big square which is made up of 25 equal small squares. How long is one side of the big square?

2 Draw one big square which is made up of 64 equal small squares. How long is one side of the big square?

3 (a) Copy and draw the next 2 shapes in this pattern.

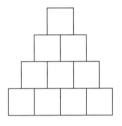

(b) Write down the number of squares for each shape in your pattern.

(c) Write down the next four numbers in this *triangular number* pattern.

E

Work out

1 7^2 **2** 10^2 **3** 12^2 **4** 20^2 **5** 15^2

6 Find   (a) $2^2 - 3$ (b) $3^2 - 6$ (c) $4^2 - 10$ (d) $5^2 - 15$

(e) $6^2 - 21$ (f) $7^2 - 28$ (g) $8^2 - 36$ (h) $9^2 - 45$

(i) What do you notice about all your answers to this question?

NUMBER SEQUENCES 2 —————————————————————

M

Write the next three numbers for each sequence and write down the rule.

1 73, 68, 63, 58

2 91, 87, 83, 79

3 25, 33, 41, 49

4 40, 55, 70, 85

5 41, 50, 59, 68

6 190, 170, 150, 130

7 150, 144, 138, 132

8 39, 50, 61, 72

9 48, 51, 54, 57

10 36, 43, 50, 57

11 110, 133, 156, 179

12 146, 141, 136, 131

13 50, 90, 130, 170

14 97, 85, 73, 61

15 200, 175, 150, 125

16 230, 275, 320, 365

17 290, 275, 260, 245

18 505, 450, 395, 340

E

Copy and complete each number sequence.

1 5 4 3 ☐ ☐ ☐ –1 –2

2 –8 ☐ –4 ☐ 0 2 4

3 –3 ☐ ☐ 0 1 2 ☐

4 0 –1 –2 ☐ ☐ ☐ –6

5 4 2 0 –2 ☐ ☐ ☐

6 –9 – 8 –7 ☐ ☐ ☐

7 9 6 3 0 ☐ ☐ ☐

8 –12 –8 ☐ 0 4 ☐

Copy and complete.

9 3 1 –1 ☐ ☐ ☐ –9

10 –7 –5 ☐ ☐ ☐ 3 5

11 10 7 4 1 ☐ ☐ ☐

12 20 15 10 5 ☐ ☐ ☐

13 –11 –8 –5 ☐ ☐ ☐ 7

14 39 29 19 9 ☐ ☐ ☐

15 15 11 7 3 ☐ ☐ ☐

16 –14 –10 –6 ☐ ☐ ☐ 10

SQUARE NUMBERS AND SQUARE ROOTS ———————— **Main Book page 125**

Remember: The *square root* of a number is the number which is multiplied by itself to give that number. The symbol for square root is $\sqrt{}$.

$$\sqrt{16} = 4 \qquad \sqrt{49} = 7$$

M

Work out

1 $2^2 + 3^2$ **2** $7^2 + 4^2$ **3** $5^2 + 3^2$ **4** $7^2 + 6^2$

5 $8^2 - 4^2$ **6** $9^2 - 5^2$ **7** $10^2 - 7^2$ **8** $6^2 - 5^2$

Work out the following. You can use a calculator.

9 $\sqrt{25}$ **10** $\sqrt{144}$ **11** $\sqrt{81}$ **12** $\sqrt{1}$

13 $\sqrt{225}$ **14** $\sqrt{64}$ **15** $\sqrt{100} - \sqrt{9}$ **16** $\sqrt{169} - \sqrt{100}$

17 $\sqrt{400} - \sqrt{25}$ **18** $\sqrt{121} + \sqrt{49}$ **19** $\sqrt{36} + \sqrt{4}$ **20** $\sqrt{196} - \sqrt{121}$

E

Use a calculator to find out which number, when multiplied by itself, gives a product of:

1 676   **2** 324   **3** 961   **4** 1849   **5** 1296

6 The area of this square is 289 cm². How long is one of its sides?

Use a calculator to work out:

7 19^2 **8** 32^2 **9** 27^2 **10** 44^2 **11** 53^2

12 What is the total area of these two squares?

16 cm, 16 cm

14 cm, 14 cm

13 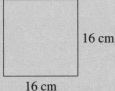 Find the shaded area.

24 cm, 24 cm, 7 cm, 7 cm

72

M

Plot the points given and join them up in order. Write down what the picture is.

1 Draw axes with values from 0 to 10.

(a) (6, 7), (6, 2), (5, 2), (5, 3)

(b) (2, 6), (2, 7), (3, 8), (5, 9), (7, 9), (9, 8), (10, 7), (10, 6), (9, 7), (8, 7), (7, 8), (6, 7), (5, 8), (4, 7), (3, 7), (2, 6)

2 Draw the horizontal axis from 0 to 14 and the vertical axis from 0 to 10.

(a) (5, 5), (5, 6), (11, 6), (11, 5)

(b) (7, 6), (7, 7), (8, 7), (8, 6)

(c) $(5\frac{1}{2}, 7)$, $(5\frac{1}{2}, 8)$, (4, 8), (4, 9)

(d) (5, 6), (5, 7), (6, 7), (6, 6)

(e) $(7\frac{1}{2}, 7)$, $(7\frac{1}{2}, 8)$, (6, 8), (6, 9)

(f) (12, 4), (2, 4), (3, 2), (12, 2), (14, 4), (12, 4), (12, 5), (4, 5), (4, 4)

(g) Draw dots at $(5, 4\frac{1}{2})$, $(6, 4\frac{1}{2})$, $(7, 4\frac{1}{2})$, $(8, 4\frac{1}{2})$, $(9, 4\frac{1}{2})$, $(10, 4\frac{1}{2})$, $(11, 4\frac{1}{2})$, $(6, 5\frac{1}{2})$, $(7, 5\frac{1}{2})$, $(8, 5\frac{1}{2})$, $(9, 5\frac{1}{2})$, $(10, 5\frac{1}{2})$

E

1
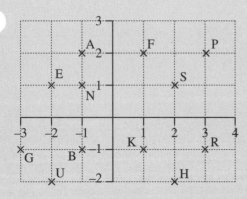

Write down the letter at each of the coordinates given below to spell a word.

(2, 1)(−2, −2)(3, 2)(−2, 1)(3, −1)

2 Draw the horizontal axis from −8 to 8 and the vertical axis from −5 to 5. Plot the points below and join them up in order. Write down what the picture is.

(a) (4, −3), (5, −3), (4, −1)

(b) (−2, −3), (−1, −3), (−1, 0), (3, −1), (3, −4), (4, −4), (4, −1) $(5, \frac{1}{2})$, $(7\frac{1}{2}, \frac{1}{2})$, $(7\frac{1}{2}, 3)$, (7, 3), (7, 1), (5, 1) (4, 2), (−2, 3), (−2, 4), (−3, 5), (−3, 4), (−6, 3), (−6, 2), (−5, 2) (−6, 1), (−3, 2), (−3, −4), (−2, −4), (−2, −1) (−1, 0)

(c) Draw a dot at (−4, 3). Colour me in.

UNIT 4

| REFLECTIVE SYMMETRY 1 | Main Book page 134 |

M

1 Copy each shape below and mark on each diagram all the lines of symmetry.

(a)
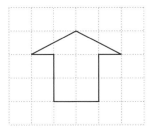

(b)
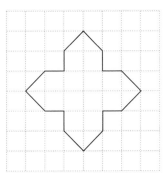

(c)
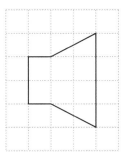

(d)
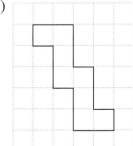

(e)
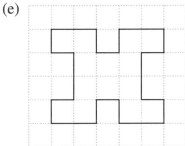

(f)
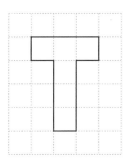

2
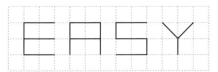
Which of these letters has no line of symmetry?

E

Copy the patterns below onto squared paper. Shade in as many squares as necessary so that the final pattern has mirror lines shown by the broken lines.

1
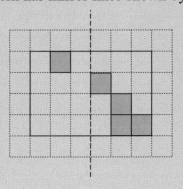

2
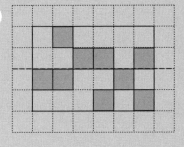

3
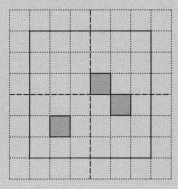

REFLECTIONS 1 ——————————————————————— **Main Book page 136**

M

Copy the shape and the mirror line and sketch the reflection.

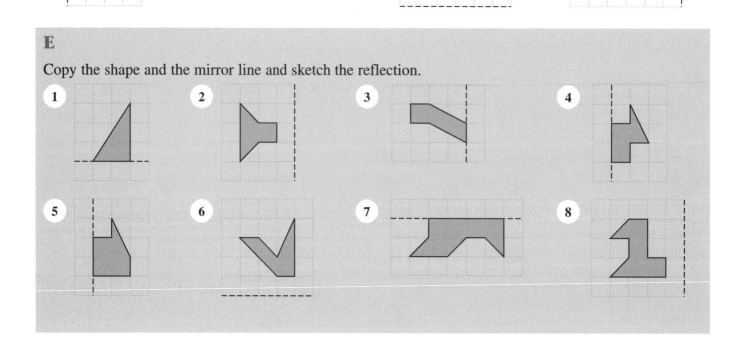

E

Copy the shape and the mirror line and sketch the reflection.

'translating' a shape means 'moving it in a straight line'.

M

1

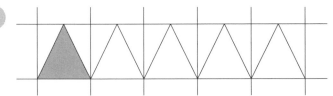

The shaded triangle above is repeatedly translated one square horizontally.

(a) Translate ▱ repeatedly one square in a horizontal line.

(b) Translate ▱ repeatedly one square in a vertical line.

(c) Translate ▱ repeatedly one square in a vertical line.

(d) Translate ◇ repeatedly 2 squares in a horizontal line.

(e) Translate ◣ repeatedly $\frac{1}{2}$ square in a horizontal line.

2 Make 3 more patterns like those done in question **1**.

E

1 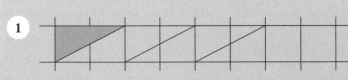 The shaded square is repeatedly translated 2 squares. Continue the pattern by showing 6 triangles.

2 Use the same shape as in question **1** and repeatedly translate it:

(a) $\frac{1}{2}$ square in a horizontal line   (b) 2 squares in a vertical line

(c) 1 square in a horizontal line   (d) $\frac{1}{2}$ square in a vertical line

3 Make a shape inside 3 squares. Starting with this shape, make 2 more patterns like those done in question **2**

M

Use a protractor to measure these angles.

Use a ruler and protractor to draw the angles below. Write *acute* or *obtuse* by each angle.

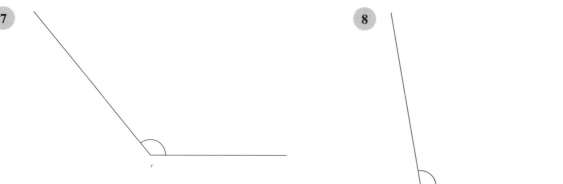

9 70°   **10** 60°   **11** 150°   **12** 80°   **13** 130°   **14** 110°

E

1 State if each angle shown is 'true' or 'false'. Do not measure the angles.

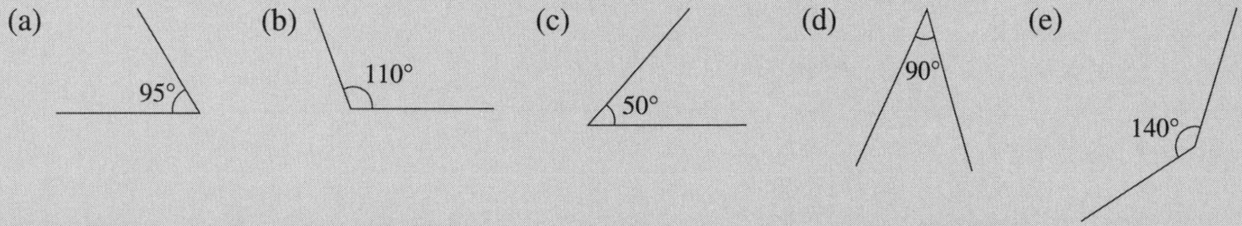

(a) 95° (b) 110° (c) 50° (d) 90° (e) 140°

Use a protractor and ruler to draw the angles below. Write acute or obtuse by each angle.

2 65°   **3** 35°   **4** 135°   **5** 165°   **6** 85°   **7** 105°

Use a protractor to measure these angles.

8

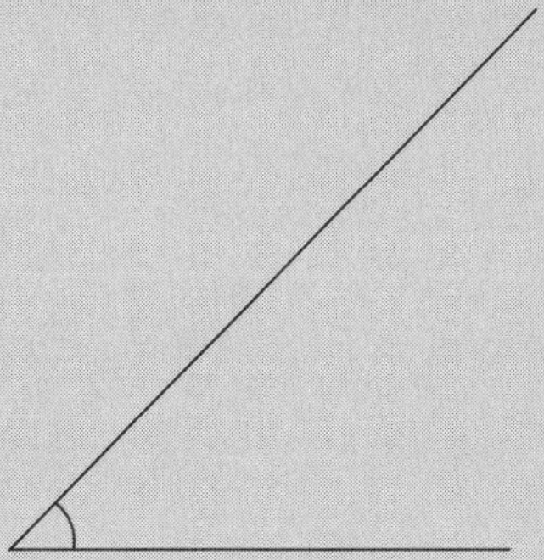

9

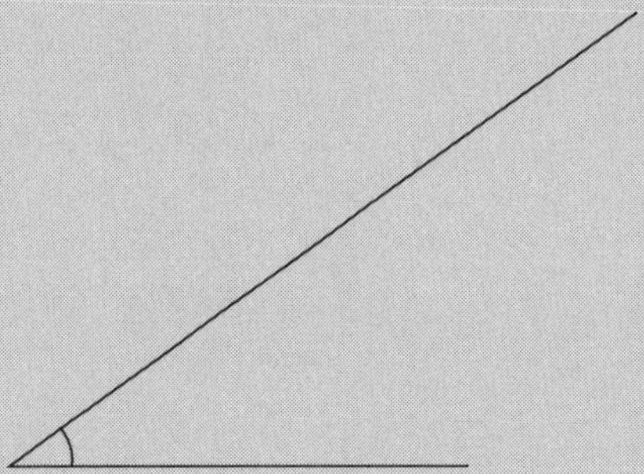

10

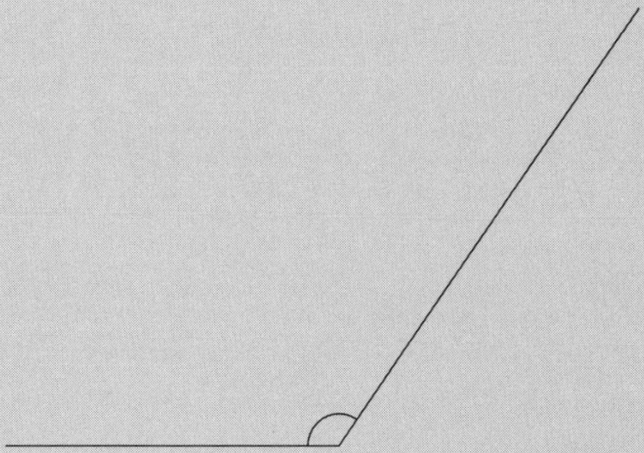

11

12

13

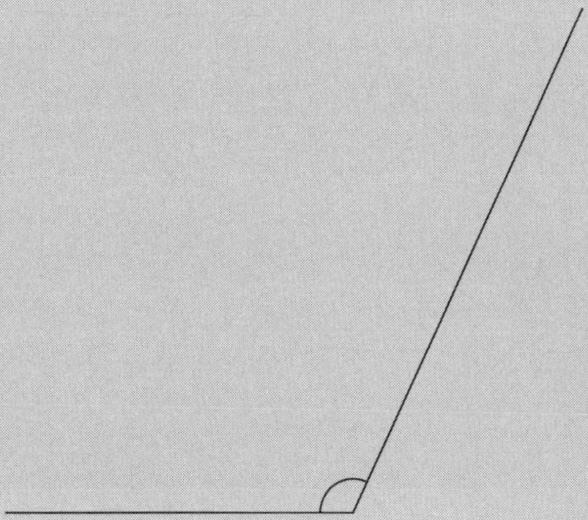

ANGLES ON A STRAIGHT LINE

$a + b = 180°$

angles on a straight line add up to 180°

M

Calculate the missing angles.

1

2

3

4

5

6

7

8

9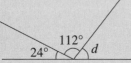

10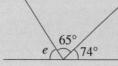

11

12

E

Calculate the missing angles.

1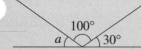

2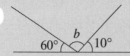

3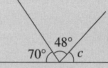

4

5

6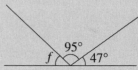

7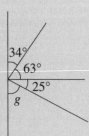

8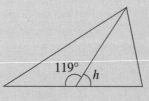

9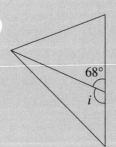

M

Calculate the missing angles.

1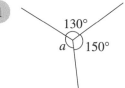

2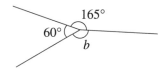

3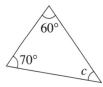

4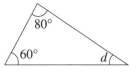

5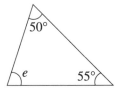

6

7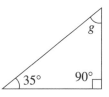

8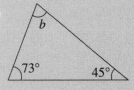

9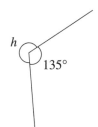

E

Calculate the missing angles.

1

2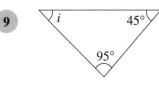

3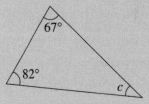

4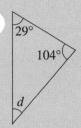

5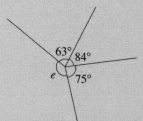

6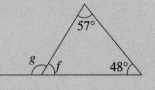

7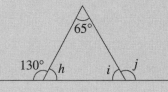

8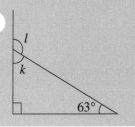

9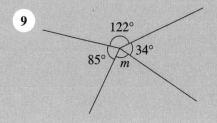

M

1 For each shape below, what fraction has been shaded?

(a)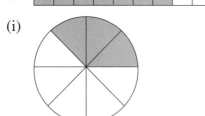

(b)

(c)

(d)

(e)

(f)

(g)

(h)

(i)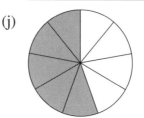

(j)

2 What fraction of one whole pizza do you get if

(a) one pizza is divided equally into 5 pieces and you are given 3 pieces

(b) one pizza is divided equally into 9 pieces and you are given 5 pieces

(c) one pizza is divided equally into 8 pieces and you are given 1 piece

(d) one pizza is divided equally into 6 pieces and you are given 5 pieces?

3 $3 \div 11 = \dfrac{3}{11}$ Write each division below as a fraction.

(a) $5 \div 8$ (b) $4 \div 9$ (c) $7 \div 10$ (d) $9 \div 20$

(e) $8 \div 15$ (f) $3 \div 7$ (g) $5 \div 6$ (h) $2 \div 3$

E

1 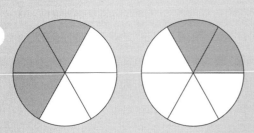 What fraction of *one* whole circle is shaded in total?

2 A toffee bar is made up from 9 equal squares.

If two toffee bars are broken into squares, what fraction of *one* whole toffee bar would you have if you are given

(a) one square from each

(b) three squares from each

(c) four squares from each

(d) two squares from each

3 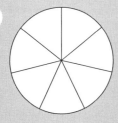 Naomi has two pizzas.

Each pizza is cut into seven equal slices.

What fraction of *one* whole pizza does Naomi eat if she takes

(a) two slices from each pizza

(b) one slice from one pizza and 2 from the other pizza

(c) two slices from one pizza and 3 from the other pizza

(d) three slices from one pizza and 4 from the other pizza

FRACTIONS OF QUANTITIES 2 ———————————— **Main Book page 147**

M

1 Find $\frac{1}{2}$ of:

(a) 32   (b) 46   (c) 14 p   (d) 26 p   (e) 70 cm   (f) 300 cm

2 Find $\frac{1}{10}$ of:

(a) 60   (b) 70   (c) 40 p   (d) 30 p   (e) 90 cm   (f) 120 cm

3 Find $\frac{1}{5}$ of:

(a) 25   (b) 10   (c) 45 p   (d) 30 p   (e) 55 cm   (f) 60 cm

4 Work out

(a) $\frac{1}{2}$ of 24   (b) $\frac{1}{4}$ of 24   (c) $\frac{1}{3}$ of 12   (d) $\frac{1}{3}$ of 21   (e) $\frac{1}{10}$ of 80 cm

(f) $\frac{1}{5}$ of 40 p   (g) $\frac{1}{4}$ of 32 p   (h) $\frac{1}{3}$ of 15 cm

---

E

1 Work out

(a) $\frac{2}{5}$ of 15   (b) $\frac{3}{5}$ of 35   (c) $\frac{3}{4}$ of 36   (d) $\frac{5}{6}$ of 12

(e) $\frac{7}{10}$ of 300   (f) $\frac{5}{9}$ of 27   (g) $\frac{3}{8}$ of 16   (h) $\frac{3}{10}$ of 70

(i) $\frac{3}{4}$ of 20   (j) $\frac{5}{8}$ of 48   (k) $\frac{4}{5}$ of 30   (l) $\frac{4}{9}$ of 54

2 Margaret has 40 sweets. She eats $\frac{7}{8}$ of the sweets. How many sweets does she have left?

3 What fraction of:

(a) £1 is 5p?   (b) £1 is 50p?   (c) £2 is 50p?

(d) 1 m is 25 cm?   (e) 2 m is 10 cm?   (f) 4 m is 40 cm?

4 60 children are asked if they have a mobile phone. Two-thirds say they have a mobile phone. How many children do *not* have a mobile phone?

FRACTIONS AND DECIMALS

Remember: $\frac{2}{10} = 0.2$ $\frac{3}{100} = 0.03$ $\frac{69}{100} = 0.69$

M

1 Write as fractions.

(a) 0.7   (b) 0.3   (c) 0.8   (d) 0.75   (e) 0.4

2 Write as decimals.

(a) $\frac{1}{10}$ (b) $\frac{9}{10}$ (c) $\frac{1}{4}$ (d) $\frac{6}{10}$ (e) $\frac{3}{4}$

3 Which is larger? $\frac{7}{10}$ or   0.6

4 Which is larger?   £0.60   or   6p

5 Which is larger?   £0.08   or   70p

6 Copy and complete this table

fraction	$\frac{3}{10}$	$\frac{8}{10}$			$\frac{1}{2}$		$\frac{7}{10}$
decimal			0.6	0.25		0.2	

E

Express each shaded area as:

(a) a fraction   (b) a decimal   (c) a percentage

1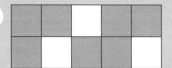

2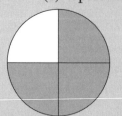

3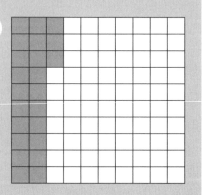

4 Write as decimals.

(a) $6\frac{1}{2}$ (b) $4\frac{9}{10}$ (c) $2\frac{3}{10}$ (d) $6\frac{3}{4}$ (e) $3\frac{9}{100}$

5 Write as whole numbers and fractions. (Example: $4.7 = 4\frac{7}{10}$)

(a) 8.9   (b) 6.75   (c) 9.37   (d) 5.03   (e) 4.91

M

Copy and complete these sentences.

1 (a) 1 in every ☐ squares is shaded.

(b) There are ☐ white squares to every 1 shaded square.

2 (a) 1 in every ☐ squares is shaded.

(b) There are ☐ white squares to every 1 shaded square.

3 (a) 1 in every ☐ squares is shaded.

(b) There are ☐ white squares to every 1 shaded square.

4 Draw a tile pattern like those above in which:

(a) 1 in every 4 squares is shaded.

(b) There are 4 white squares to every shaded square.

5 Copy this diagram. Shade some squares so that for every 2 white squares there are 3 shaded squares.

E

1 Janet has five times as much money as Ben. Ben has £7. How much money does Janet have?

2 In class 7C there is one boy for every two girls. There are 20 girls in class 7C. How many boys are there?

3 In a box of chocolates there are 4 plain for every 3 milk. There are 14 chocolates. How many plain chocolates are there?

4 Mark scores in one out of every 3 football matches he plays in. How many matches will he score in if he plays in 24 matches?

5 Wendy is half the age of Marcus. Marcus is 38 years old. How old is Wendy?

6 Two in every nine people who come into a post office wear glasses. 36 people came into the post office. How many people were wearing glasses?

IMPROPER FRACTIONS 2 ————————————————————

M

Remember: $\dfrac{7}{4} = 7 \div 4 = 1\dfrac{3}{4}$ $\qquad$ $3\dfrac{1}{2} = \dfrac{7}{2}$

$\quad$ improper $\qquad$ mixed
$\quad$ fraction $\qquad$ number

Write the shaded areas as both mixed numbers and improper fractions.

1 $\qquad$ 2 $\qquad$ 3

4 $\qquad$ 5 $\qquad$ 6

7 $\qquad$ 8 $\qquad$ 9

Copy and complete.

10 $\quad 2\dfrac{1}{2} = \dfrac{\square}{2}$ $\qquad$ 11 $\quad 1\dfrac{5}{6} = \dfrac{\square}{6}$ $\qquad$ 12 $\quad 5\dfrac{1}{4} = \dfrac{\square}{4}$ $\qquad$ 13 $\quad 3\dfrac{3}{4} = \dfrac{15}{\square}$ $\qquad$ 14 $\quad 2\dfrac{3}{5} = \dfrac{\square}{\square}$

15 $\quad \dfrac{25}{8} = 3\dfrac{\square}{8}$ $\qquad$ 16 $\quad \dfrac{37}{8} = \square\dfrac{\square}{8}$ $\qquad$ 17 $\quad \dfrac{29}{10} = \square\dfrac{\square}{10}$ $\qquad$ 18 $\quad \dfrac{32}{5} = \square\dfrac{2}{\square}$ $\qquad$ 19 $\quad \dfrac{17}{3} = \square\dfrac{\square}{\square}$

E

Change to mixed numbers.

1 $\quad \dfrac{19}{5}$ $\qquad$ 2 $\quad \dfrac{13}{8}$ $\qquad$ 3 $\quad \dfrac{16}{7}$ $\qquad$ 4 $\quad \dfrac{29}{6}$ $\qquad$ 5 $\quad \dfrac{29}{9}$

6 $\quad \dfrac{27}{4}$ $\qquad$ 7 $\quad \dfrac{7}{3}$ $\qquad$ 8 $\quad \dfrac{17}{4}$ $\qquad$ 9 $\quad \dfrac{33}{10}$ $\qquad$ 10 $\quad \dfrac{26}{3}$

Change to improper fractions.

11 $\quad 4\dfrac{5}{7}$ $\qquad$ 12 $\quad 5\dfrac{1}{2}$ $\qquad$ 13 $\quad 6\dfrac{7}{8}$ $\qquad$ 14 $\quad 6\dfrac{1}{6}$ $\qquad$ 15 $\quad 7\dfrac{5}{9}$

16 $\quad 3\dfrac{5}{6}$ $\qquad$ 17 $\quad 8\dfrac{4}{5}$ $\qquad$ 18 $\quad 10\dfrac{3}{4}$ $\qquad$ 19 $\quad 7\dfrac{3}{5}$ $\qquad$ 20 $\quad 5\dfrac{2}{9}$

21 $\quad$ Which is larger? $\qquad \left(\dfrac{13}{2} \quad \text{or} \quad \dfrac{25}{4} \right)$

22 $\quad$ Which is larger? $\qquad \left(\dfrac{31}{4} \quad \text{or} \quad \dfrac{42}{5} \right)$

ORDERING FRACTIONS ───────────────────────────

Remember: $\frac{1}{3} = \frac{2}{6}$ and $\frac{1}{2} = \frac{3}{6}$ so $\frac{1}{2}$ is greater than $\frac{1}{3}$

M

1 Which is the larger of each pair of fractions?

(a) $\frac{2}{5}$ or $\frac{3}{10}$ (b) $\frac{5}{8}$ or $\frac{1}{2}$ (c) $\frac{2}{3}$ or $\frac{3}{4}$

(d) $\frac{1}{4}$ or $\frac{1}{6}$ (e) $\frac{3}{5}$ or $\frac{3}{4}$ (f) $\frac{1}{2}$ or $\frac{5}{12}$

2 Place in order, smallest first.

(a) $\frac{1}{2}, \frac{1}{3}, \frac{5}{6}$ (b) $\frac{5}{12}, \frac{1}{4}, \frac{1}{3}$ (c) $\frac{7}{10}, \frac{3}{4}, \frac{3}{5}$

E

1 Match the fractions to the letters.

```
   A        B      C D   E F      G   H
```

| $\frac{3}{5}$ | $\frac{1}{2}$ | $\frac{3}{10}$ | $\frac{9}{20}$ | $\frac{4}{5}$ | $\frac{13}{20}$ | $\frac{1}{10}$ | $\frac{9}{10}$ |

2 Place in order, smallest first.

(a) $\frac{7}{12}, \frac{3}{4}, \frac{2}{3}$ (b) $\frac{5}{9}, \frac{1}{3}, \frac{1}{2}$

(c) $\frac{7}{10}, \frac{4}{5}, \frac{3}{4}$ (d) $1\frac{1}{2}, 1\frac{1}{4}, 1\frac{1}{3}$

(e) $1\frac{1}{3}, 1\frac{1}{6}, 1\frac{2}{9}, 1\frac{1}{9}$

(f) $2\frac{3}{4}, 2, 2\frac{1}{2}, 2\frac{11}{12}$

M

1 Find 50% of:

(a) 20   (b) 50   (c) 80   (d) 10   (e) 200

2 Find 25% of:

(a) 40   (b) 16   (c) 28   (d) 80   (e) 36

3 Find 10% of:

(a) 60   (b) 20   (c) 70   (d) 200   (e) 80

4 Find 20% of:

(a) 60   (b) 20   (c) 70   (d) 200   (e) 80

Work out

5 10% of 30   **6** 20% of 30   **7** 50% of 32

8 25% of 32   **9** 25% of 44   **10** 20% of 300

E

Work out

1 50% of 16   **2** 25% of 48   **3** 10% of 90

4 20% of 90   **5** 30% of 90   **6** 75% of 24

7 30% of 40   **8** 40% of 50   **9** 5% of 60

10 75% of 80   **11** 5% of 400   **12** 40% of 70

13 Jack earns £320 each week. One week he is paid an extra 25%. How much money is he paid in that week?

14 Find 25% of 84p   **15** Find 75% of £28   **16** Find 20% of £120

17 Find 10% of £1.60   **18** Find 50% of £2.60   **19** Find 30% of £3.60

M

1 Double these numbers.

(a) 230   (b) 65   (c) 350   (d) 17   (e) 36   (f) 75

2 Halve these numbers.

(a) 300   (b) 340   (c) 110   (d) 900   (e) 28   (f) 52

3 Find one quarter of:

(a) 240   (b) 32   (c) 840   (d) 36   (e) 160   (f) 2000

5 Copy and complete by doubling.

(a) $1 \times 30 = \square$ (b) $1 \times 45 = \square$ (c) $1 \times 70 = \square$
$2 \times 30 = \square$ $2 \times 45 = \square$ $2 \times 70 = \square$
$4 \times 30 = \square$ $4 \times 45 = \square$ $4 \times 70 = \square$
$8 \times 30 = \square$ $8 \times 45 = \square$ $8 \times 70 = \square$
$16 \times 30 = \square$ $16 \times 45 = \square$ $16 \times 70 = \square$

E

1 Double these numbers.

(a) 47   (b) 4000   (c) 38   (d) 78   (e) 2500   (f) 3700
(g) 57   (h) 7300   (i) 4900   (j) 56   (k) 280   (l) 8700

2 Halve then find one quarter of:

(a) 56   (b) 380   (c) 8600   (d) 96   (e) 7200   (f) 640

3 Find $\frac{1}{8}$ of:

(a) 56   (b) 320   (c) 800   (d) 720   (e) 2400   (f) 6400

4 (a) Copy and complete by doubling.

$1 \times 14 = \square$, $2 \times 14 = \square$, $4 \times 14 = \square$, $8 \times 14 = \square$, $16 \times 14 = \square$

Use these answers to work out
(b) 5×14 (c) 17×14 (d) 34×14

M

Work out

1 $14 \times 3 = (10 \times 3) + (4 \times 3) = 30 + 12 =$

   2 $16 \times 3 = (10 \times 3) + (6 \times 3) =$

     3 $13 \times 4 = (10 \times 4) + (3 \times 4) =$

       4 $18 \times 4 = (10 \times 4) + (8 \times 4) =$

      5 $22 \times 4 = (20 \times 4) + (2 \times 4) =$

     6 $34 \times 3 = (30 \times 3) + (4 \times 3) =$

     7 $43 \times 4 = (40 \times 4) + (3 \times 4) =$

      8 $46 \times 4 = (40 \times 4) + (6 \times 4) =$

     9 $36 \times 4 = (30 \times 4) + (6 \times 4) =$

    10 $23 \times 4 = (20 \times 4) + (3 \times 4) =$

11   Work out

   (a) 13×3 (b) 21×4 (c) 14×5 (d) 32×4 (e) 14×4

   (f) 22×3 (g) 34×4 (h) 23×3 (i) 33×5 (j) 12×5

E

Work out

1 37×6 **2** 47×8 **3** 46×6 **4** 53×9 **5** 74×7

6 54×7 **7** 62×4 **8** 93×8 **9** 49×6 **10** 68×9

11 58×6 **12** 76×9 **13** 84×7 **14** 58×7 **15** 38×8

16   An octopus has 8 legs. This octopus has 16 octopus friends. How many legs do they *all* have in total?

17   57 children each pay £6 to see a play. How much do they pay in total?

M

Copy and complete by writing the missing number in the box.

1. $5 \times \square = 30$
2. $3 \times \square = 18$
3. $\square \times 3 = 24$
4. $\square \times 4 = 20$

5. $\square \times 6 = 24$
6. $7 \times \square = 35$
7. $9 \times \square = 36$
8. $\square \times 7 = 28$

9. $8 \times \square = 32$
10. $\square \times 6 = 0$
11. $7 \times \square = 42$
12. $\square \times 8 = 56$

13. $\boxed{2} \xrightarrow{\times} \boxed{} \xrightarrow{=} \boxed{8} \xrightarrow{\times} \boxed{} \xrightarrow{=} \boxed{48}$

14. $\boxed{} \xrightarrow{\times} \boxed{3} \xrightarrow{=} \boxed{9} \xrightarrow{\times} \boxed{} \xrightarrow{=} \boxed{63}$

15. If $8 \times 9 = 72$ then $72 \div \square = 8$

E

Copy and complete.

1. $8 \times \square = 56$
2. $\square \times 7 = 49$
3. $\square \times 2 = 50$
4. $5 \times \square = 100$

5. $\square \times 8 = 200$
6. $\square \times 3 = 120$
7. $9 \times \square = 0$
8. $\square \times 12 = 360$

Copy and complete these multiplication squares.

9.

×		6	
8	24		32
		30	
			28

10.

×	6		
		18	72
7		14	
	36		

11.

×			
		45	
	28		32
		35	56

STANDARD METHOD FOR MULTIPLICATION ────────

M

Work out

1 218
× 4

2 326
× 6

3 539
× 3

4 268
× 7

5 532
× 6

6 147
× 8

7 374
× 5

8 293
× 8

9 613
× 9

10 458
× 4

11 267
× 6

12 194
× 7

13 743
× 5

14 826
× 7

15 458
× 9

16 922
× 6

E

Work out

1 5.4
× 3

2 4.4
× 3

3 3.6
× 5

4 2.8
× 6

5 7.6
× 4

6 3.9
× 5

7 5.3
× 7

8 6.9
× 8

9 Charlie travels 2.6 km to work each day.
How far does he travel in 6 days?

10 A bag of potatoes weighs 3.6 kg.
How much do 7 bags weigh?

Work out

11 4.2×6

12 7.4×3

13 1.9×9

14 5.3×7

15 6.6×8

16 3.7×9

17 6.2×6

18 8.2×7

M

Work out

1 $2\overline{)32}$ **2** $6\overline{)78}$ **3** $4\overline{)52}$ **4** $5\overline{)75}$

5 $4\overline{)84}$ **6** $3\overline{)72}$ **7** $6\overline{)192}$ **8** $9\overline{)153}$

9 $150 \div 6$ **10** $170 \div 5$ **11** $224 \div 8$ **12** $88 \div 4$

13 $135 \div 5$ **14** $231 \div 7$ **15** $96 \div 6$ **16** $207 \div 9$

17 Murphy travels 252 miles in his van during 7 days. How for does he travel each day if he travels the same distance each day?

18 192 screws are divided equally into 8 packs. How many screws are there in each pack?

E

Work out

1 $189 \div 7$ **2** $234 \div 6$ **3** $405 \div 9$ **4** $423 \div 9$

5 $416 \div 8$ **6** $366 \div 6$ **7** $152 \div 4$ **8** $322 \div 7$

9 $486 \div 9$ **10** $220 \div 5$ **11** $522 \div 9$ **12** $392 \div 8$

13 $434 \div 7$ **14** $392 \div 7$ **15** $276 \div 6$ **16** $513 \div 9$

17 Nine barrels are filled with a total of 234 litres of milk. How much milk does one barrel contain?

18 £402 is shared equally between 6 people. How much does each person get?

LONG MULTIPLICATION 3 ————————————

M

Work out

1   13
  × 15

2   22
  × 13

3   14
  × 24

4   34
  × 21

5 25 × 14

6 12 × 33

7 42 × 22

8 31 × 24

9 43 × 32

10 32 × 13

11 45 × 23

12 23 × 35

E

Work out

1   46
  × 52

2   63
  × 48

3   84
  × 62

4   79
  × 65

5 39 × 53

6 71 × 87

7 96 × 47

8 68 × 44

9   68 people each pay £49 for a theatre trip. How much do they pay in total?

10 Each bottle bank contains 98 bottles when full.
    How many bottles will fill 28 bottle banks?

11 Copy and complete this multiplication square.

×	36	24	68
48			
35			
74			

DIVISIBILITY TESTS ————————————————————

Whole numbers are divisible by:
  100 if the last two digits are 00.
   10 if the last digit is 0.
    2 if the number is even.
    4 if the last two digits are divisible by 4.
    5 if the last digit is 0 or 5.
    3 if the sum of the digits is divisible by 3.

M

1 Which of these numbers is divisible by 10?

82	40	70	47	1300	89

2 Which of the numbers below is divisible by 5?

45	200	36	820	59	615

3 Which of the numbers below is divisible by 4?

32	732	606	512	739	417

4 Which of the numbers below is divisible by 3?

27	134	216	408	319	527

5 Write true or false:

(a) 73 is divisible by 2   (b) 1600 is divisible by 100   (c) 249 is divisible by 3

(d) 462 is divisible by 4   (e) 174 is divisible by 2   (f) 723 is divisible by 5

E

Copy and complete the table, using ticks and crosses to show divisibility.

Number	Divisible by				
	2	3	4	5	10
632	✓	✗	✓	✗	✗
516					
700					
921					
649					
1210					
1960					

USING LETTER SYMBOLS 3 ───────── **Main Book page 162**

Example. Add the numbers or letters on the two lower bricks and write the answer above.

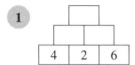 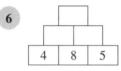

M

Copy and fill in each empty box like the examples above.

1 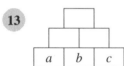   **2** 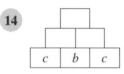   **3** 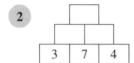   **4**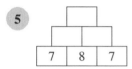

5 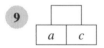   **6**   **7**   **8**

In questions **9** to **16**   a = 5, b = 3 and c = 6. Copy and fill in each empty box.

9   **10**   **11** 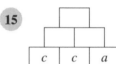   **12**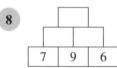

13 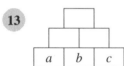   **14** 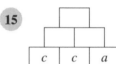   **15** 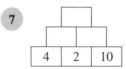   **16**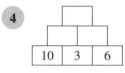

E

Use letters only to copy and fill in the empty boxes.

1 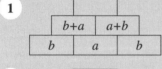   **2** 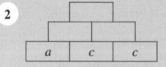   **3**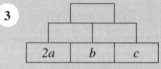

4 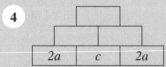   **5** 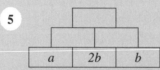   **6**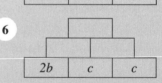

7 What is the number in the top box in question **2** if a = 4 and c = 7?

8 What is the number in the top box in question **5** if a = 3 and b = 8?

9 (a) Copy and fill in each empty box using letters.

(b) What number is in the top box if a = 6, b = 5 and c = 7?

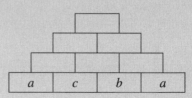

THE FOUR OPERATIONS 2

M

What number belongs in the empty box?

1 □ → +9 → 16   2 □ → +5 → 21

3 □ → +16 → 27   4 □ → +13 → 42

5 □ → +8 → 32   6 □ → −6 → 12

7 □ → −19 → 23   8 □ → −12 → 26

9 □ → −24 → 31   10 □ → −17 → 18

11 □ → ×3 → 18   12 □ → ×2 → 28

13 □ → ×4 → 32   14 □ → ×6 → 36

15 □ → ×5 → 45   16 □ → ÷5 → 8

17 □ → ÷4 → 7   18 □ → ÷3 → 9

19 □ → ÷6 → 8   20 □ → ÷4 → 6

E

What number belongs in the empty box?

1 □ → +28 → 66   2 □ → −29 → 71

3 □ → −36 → 49   4 □ → +32 → 61

5 □ → −43 → 28   6 □ → +53 → 72

7 □ → +74 → 93   8 □ → −37 → 56

9 □ → −65 → 27   10 □ → +88 → 95

11 □ → ×7 → 182   12 □ → ÷4 → 9

13 □ → ×9 → 162   14 □ → ×8 → 192

15 □ → ÷7 → 8   16 □ → ÷6 → 5

17 □ → ÷6 → 9   18 □ → ×11 → 132

19 □ → ×20 → 340   20 □ → ÷30 → 4

COLLECTING LIKE TERMS 2 —————————————

Remember: $5m + 3n + n + 4m = 9m + 4n$ $5m + 3$ cannot be simplified

M

Collect like terms where possible.

1 $m + 4n + 2m$ **2** $3a + 4a + 2b$ **3** $p + 3q + p$

4 $f + 2g + 3f$ **5** $5x + 4y + 2x$ **6** $3a + a + 2b + 2a$

7 $6r + 4s + 3s$ **8** $2m + 3m + n + 4n$ **9** $4b + 3c + 2c + 2b$

10 $7n + 4p + p + 2n$ **11** $8a + 3b + a + 3b$ **12** $5w + 3w + 6n + 2n$

13 $3p + 5q - p$ **14** $5m + 3n + 2n - 2m$ **15** $8a + 4b - 2b - 3a$

16 $3b + 4c + b - 2c$ **17** $4x + 2x + 3y - x$ **18** $4f + 2g + 3f + 7g$

19 $5w + 3w + q + w$ **20** $9a + 4b - 2a + b$ **21** $3x + 2y + 5x + 6$

22 $4m + 2m + 5p - 2p$ **23** $6y + 4w + 2 + 3w$ **24** $7a + 3b + a - b$

E

Collect like terms

1 $6m + 4n + 9m + 8n + 3n$ **2** $5a + 7b + 4a + 3b - a$ **3** $8y + 4w - 6y + 3w + w$

4 $13f + 12f + 7g - 3g + 2f$ **5** $9a + 5b + 6a - b + 3$ **6** $19x - 3x + 6y - 2y + x$

7 $12x + 6x + 9y + 8 - 3y$ **8** $16m + 9n - 7m + 3n + 4n$ **9** $23c + 19d - 6c - 8d + 4c$

10 $15a + 3a + 9b - 3b + 6a - b$ **11** $14m + 6n + 3n + 5 - 2n + 3n$ **12** $16a + 4a + 12b - 6a + 3 - 4b$

Find the perimeter of the following shapes.

13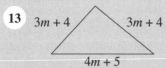

14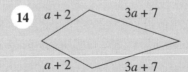

15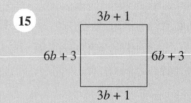

16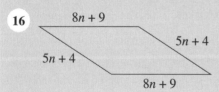

UNIT 5

M

Draw each shape below on squared paper then show all lines of symmetry.

1 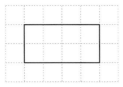 2 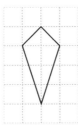 3 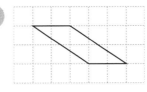 4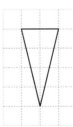

5 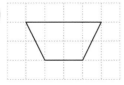 6 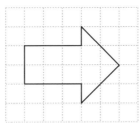 7   8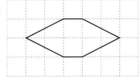

E

1 (a) Draw each shape below on squared paper then show all lines of symmetry.

   (b) Draw one letter of your own choice which has one line of symmetry only.

   (c) Draw one letter of your own choice which has no lines of symmetry.

2 Draw your own shape which has *more* than two lines of symmetry. Draw all the lines of symmetry.

M

Copy these shapes onto squared paper and sketch the reflection in the mirror line shown.

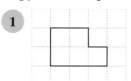
1

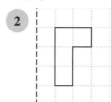
2

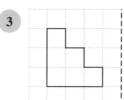
3

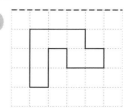
4

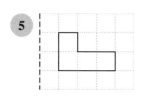
5

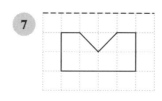
6

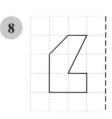
7

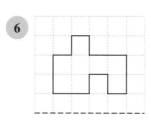
8

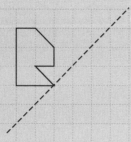
9

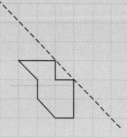
10

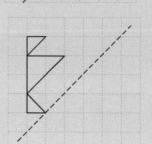
11

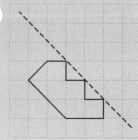
12

E

Copy each shape and mirror line onto squared paper and sketch the reflection.

1

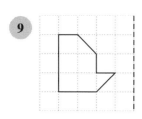
2

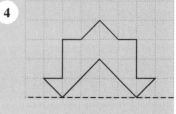
3

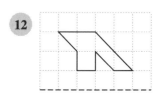
4

5

6

7

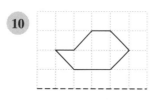
8

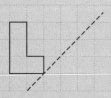
9

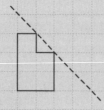
10

11

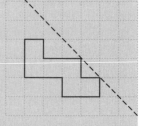
12

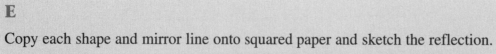

TRANSLATION 2 ────────────────────────────

Remember: 'translating' a shape means 'moving in straight line'

M

1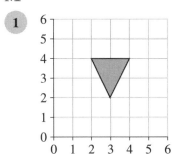

(a) Copy this grid and the triangle.

(b) Translate the trangle right 2 squares and draw the new triangle.

(c) Translate the first triangle down 2 squares and draw the new triangle.

2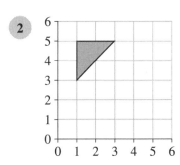

(a) Copy this grid and the triangle.

(b) Translate the triangle down 3 squares and draw the new triangle.

(c) Translate the first triangle right 2 squares and draw the new triangle.

(d) Translate the first triangle up 1 square and draw the new triangle (it will overlap the first triangle).

E

1 What shape do you move to when you:

(a) translate shape Q   2 units right, 2 units down

(b) translate shape S   2 units left, 3 units down

(c) translate shape R   6 units left, 3 units down.

(d) translate shape Q   8 units right, 2 units down.

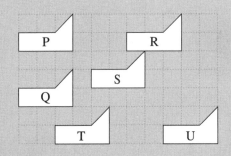

2 Describe the following translations.

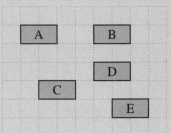

(a) A → C   (b) A → B

(c) D → A   (d) D → E

(e) B → D   (f) E → B

ROTATIONAL SYMMETRY

  This shape fits onto itself six times when rotated through a complete turn. It has *rotational symmetry* of *order* six.

M/E

For each shape write down the order of rotational symmetry.

1

2

3

4

5

6

7

8

9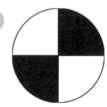

10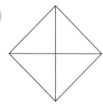

11

12

> Remember: 3, 4, 4, 6, 8
>
> median = 4 (half way),   mode = 4 (more fours than any other number)
>
> mean = $\frac{3 + 4 + 4 + 6 + 8}{5} = \frac{25}{5} = 5$
>
> range = 8 − 3 = 5 (highest number − lowest number)

M

For each list of numbers in questions **1** to **4** , find

(a) the mean   (b) the median   (c) the mode   (d) the range.

1 1, 6, 5, 3, 5

2 5, 9, 6, 11, 12, 6, 7

3 3, 7, 9, 5, 3, 9, 9, 2, 7, 9, 3

4 120, 110, 108, 112, 120

5

| 4, 6, 6, 5, 7, 5, 4 |
| 6, 5, 8, 6, 4, 8, 5 |
| 4, 5, 7, 5, 6, 7, 4 |
| 7, 8, 5, 6, 5, 4, 7 |

The shoe sizes of a class of 28 pupils are shown in this box.

Find the modal shoe size (the mode).

E

1 The ages of some dogs in a kennel were 7, 3, 5, 3, 10, 2 and the ages of some cats were 5, 6, 9, 8.

(a) Find the mean age for the dogs.   (b) Find the mean age for the cats.

(c) Find the mean age for all ten animals.

2 'The mode for the numbers 4, 3, 5, 6, 6, 8, 7, 6, 3, 5, 3, 6, 7 is 3'. Is this true or false?

3 Callum throws a dice eight times and his grandfather gives him a £1 coin if the mean score is equal to 3. The dice are shown below. Does he win £1?

4 Kyle plays a computer game nine times. His scores are shown below.

8290,   8200,   8247,   8315,   8956,   8721,   7460,   8194,   7278

Louise plays the computer game seven times. Her scores are shown below.

9478,   8493,   7638,   8004,   8195,   7419,   9316

Which player has the greater median score and by how much?

M/E

1 Here is a frequency diagram showing how many children there are in several primary schools.

(a) How many schools have between 101 and 125 children?

(b) How many schools have between 51 and 100 children?

(c) How many schools are there altogether?

(d) How many schools have less than 76 children?

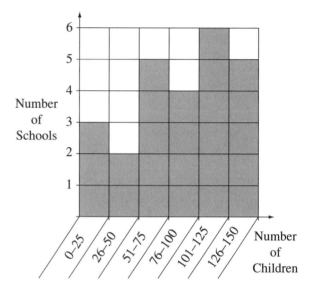

2 Some children collect Warhammer pieces. 24 children were asked how many pieces they have. The findings are shown below.

| 38 | 12 | 63 | 18 | 42 | 87 | 56 | 55 | 72 | 8 | 19 | 26 |
| 82 | 59 | 13 | 73 | 23 | 68 | 31 | 17 | 44 | 12 | 95 | 48 |

(a) Put the heights into groups.

(b) Draw a frequency diagram.

(c) How many children had between 41 and 80 pieces?

Number of pieces	Tally	Frequency
0–20	JHT II	7
21–40		
41–60		
61–80		
81–100		

3

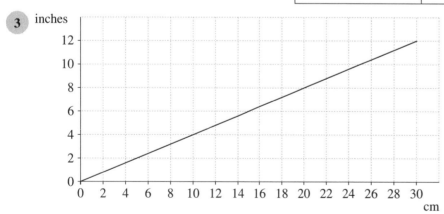

The graph above converts cm into inches.

(a) Convert into inches

    (i) 10 cm   (ii) 20 cm   (iii) 5 cm

(b) Which is longer? 15 cm or 7 inches

M

1. A bucket contains 1 green ball, 1 yellow ball and 1 red ball. One ball is chosen at random. What is the probability of choosing:

    (a) a red ball?   (b) a yellow ball?

2. A bag contains 2 red balls and 3 blue balls. If I take out one ball, what is the probability that it will be:

    (a) a blue ball?

    (b) a red ball?

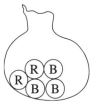

3. What is the probability of spinning a shaded part on this spinner?

4. | C | H | A | N | C | E |

    One of these letters is selected at random. What is the probability of selecting

    (a) the letter N   (b) the letter C?

5. | 2 | | 3 | One of these prime numbers is chosen at random. What is the probability of choosing

    | 5 | | 7 | | 11 |

    | 13 | | 17 |

    (a) a number less than 6   (b) a single digit number

    (c) an even number

E

1. There are 18 socks in a drawer. 8 are blue, 7 are grey and the rest are red. Jan selects a sock at random. What is the probability that she selects:

    (a) a grey sock   (b) a red sock   (c) a green sock?

2. One of these cards is selected at random. What is the probability of selecting:

    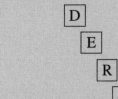

    (a) the letter R

    (b) a | ? |

    (c) a vowel?

3. A fair dice is rolled. Are you more likely to get an odd number or a number greater than 4? *Explain* your answer.

4 1 3 4 4 7 9 9 9 10 11

A card is selected at random. Find the probability of selecting

(a) a number greater than 9

(b) an even number

(c) a prime number

5 T H I N K

These cards are shuffled. One card is selected at random and turns out to be an 'H'.
What is the probability that the next selected card is a 'K'?

PROBABILITY EXPERIMENTS ———————————————— **Main Book page 182**

M/E

1 Get a shoe.

2 Spin the shoe in the air and see if it lands 'the right way up', ie. the heel on the bottom.

3 You must do this 50 times. Each time is called a 'trial' and you must record each time the shoe lands the 'right way up' (a 'success'). A tally chart like below may help.

Number of trials	Number of successes
ꟼꟼ ꟼꟼꟼ	ꟼꟼꟼ

4 Use a calculator to work out the experimental probability that a shoe will land the 'right way up' when it is thrown in the air.

Reminder:

prohability = (number of successes) ÷ (total number of trials)

5 If you did this experiment again, do you think you would get the same answer? Discuss this with your teacher when you are back in a lesson.

M

1 $18 \div 6 = 3$ with *no remainder* so 6 is a factor of 18. Write true or false for each statement below.

(a) 6 is a factor of 12   (b) 3 is a factor of 15   (c) 4 is a factor of 18   (d) 5 is a factor of 40

(e) 6 is a factor of 42   (f) 8 is a factor of 30   (g) 10 has 4 factors   (h) 16 has 4 factors

2 Copy and complete each statement below.

(a) The factors of 8 are 1, ☐, 2 and ☐.   (b) The factors of 15 are ☐, 15, 3 and ☐.

(c) The factors of 20 are 1, ☐, 2, ☐, ☐ and 5.

3 Find all the pairs of factors of   (a) 14   (b) 12   (c) 22

E

Escape

In the town of Decford a prison has 10 cells. All the cells have one prisoner in them and all the cell doors are locked.

1 Draw 10 doors as shown below.

☐1 ☐2 ☐3 ☐4 ☐5 ☐6 ☐7 ☐8 ☐9 ☐10

2 A jailer walks from cell 1 to cell 10 and unlocks each door. Show each door is unlocked by writing a 'U' under each door.

3 The jailer returns to the start and locks every second door. Show each door that is locked by using an 'L' as shown below.

1	2	3	4	5	6	7	8	9	10
U	U	U	U	U	U	U	U	U	U
	L		L		L		L		L

4 The jailer returns to the start and changes the state of every third door (ie. cells 3, 6, 9). '*Changes the state of a door*' means '*lock if unlocked*' or '*unlock if locked*'. Show on your diagram which door now has a 'U' or 'L'.

5 The jailer repeats the process for every fourth door then fifth door, sixth, seventh, eighth, ninth and finally tenth. Write a 'U' or 'L' on your diagram whenever you need to.

6 How many prisoners can now escape through an unlocked door? Write down the cell numbers of those prisoners who can escape.

MULTIPLICATION FACTS FOR 6, 7, 8, 9 ┤

M

Write the answers only.

1 60 × 6 **2** 50 × 6 **3** 400 × 6 **4** 300 × 6 **5** 20 × 6

6 180 ÷ 6 **7** 540 ÷ 6 **8** 2400 ÷ 6 **9** 360 ÷ 6 **10** 4200 ÷ 6

11 40 × 9 **12** 90 × 9 **13** 200 × 9 **14** 800 × 9 **15** 700 × 9

16 540 ÷ 9 **17** 2700 ÷ 9 **18** 630 ÷ 9 **19** 4500 ÷ 9 **20** 3600 ÷ 9

Work out

21 9 × 12 **22** 22 × 12 **23** 8 × 18 **24** 40 × 18 **25** 50 × 18

26 There are 6 pencils in a pack. How many pencils are there is 86 packs?

27 Nine people go to an adventure park for the day. Each person pays £28. How much do they pay in total?

E

Write the answers only.

1 30 × 7 **2** 40 × 7 **3** 500 × 7 **4** 900 × 7 **5** 700 × 7

6 210 ÷ 7 **7** 560 ÷ 7 **8** 1400 ÷ 7 **9** 3500 ÷ 7 **10** 6300 ÷ 7

11 70 × 8 **12** 30 × 8 **13** 400 × 8 **14** 900 × 8 **15** 800 × 8

16 480 ÷ 8 **17** 1600 ÷ 8 **18** 560 ÷ 8 **19** 6400 ÷ 8 **20** 7200 ÷ 8

Work out

21 8 × 14 **22** 20 × 14 **23** 9 × 16 **24** 60 × 16 **25** 70 × 16

26 Sid washes the windows of 17 houses. Each house has 8 windows. How many windows does Sid wash?

27 How many weeks are equal to 252 days?

Examples: $33 + 29 = 33 + 30 - 1$ $67 - 19 = 67 - 20 + 1$
$= 63 - 1$ $= 47 + 1$
$= 62$ $= 48$

M

1 Add 21 onto:

(a) 38   (b) 248   (c) 317   (d) 163   (e) 237

2 Take 19 from:

(a) 465   (b) 368   (c) 200   (d) 137   (e) 345

3 Take 39 from:

(a) 84   (b) 232   (c) 183   (d) 482   (e) 164

4 Add 49 onto:

(a) 36   (b) 175   (c) 116   (d) 312   (e) 169

5 Barry has £146. He spends £29. How much money does he now have left?

6 Copy and complete this number chain by taking away 59 each time.

416 → ☐ → ☐ → ☐ → ☐ → ☐

E

Copy and complete the addition squares.

1

+	31	49	11	16
60				
19				
41				
59				

2

+	39	36	79	61
9				
69				
25				
11				

3 Copy and complete.

(a) ☐ + 31 = 79   (b) 61 + ☐ = 115   (c) 71 + ☐ = 290

(d) ☐ + 91 = 162   (e) ☐ − 41 = 38   (f) ☐ − 61 = 49

(g) ☐ − 19 = 26   (h) ☐ − 31 = 75   (i) 29 + ☐ = 88

MENTAL STRATEGIES 5 (+ AND –) ────────────────

Examples: 47 – 35 = 5 + 7 = 12   93 – 56 = 4 + 30 + 3 = 37
          602 – 574 = 6 + 20 + 2 = 28   3006 – 2978 = 2 + 20 + 6 = 28

M

Work out

1 43 – 37   **2** 62 – 55   **3** 37 – 29   **4** 52 – 26

5 70 – 39   **6** 94 – 38   **7** 64 – 28   **8** 83 – 46

9 300 – 286   **10** 500 – 474   **11** 204 – 187   **12** 107 – 79

13  What do you add to make each number up to the target?

(a) 27   (b) 58   (c) 43   (d) 84

Work out

14 306 – 197   **15** 607 – 468   **16** 232 – 175   **17** 181 – 66

18 3000 – 2984   **19** 4000 – 3981   **20** 614 – 587   **21** 376 – 198

22  What do you add to make each number up to the target?

(a) 248   (b) 193   (c) 124   (d) 82

E

Copy and complete each number chain.

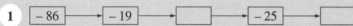

1 [– 86] → [– 19] → [ ] → [– 25] → [ ]

2 [175] → [– 98] → [ ] → [– 38] → [ ]

3 [300] → [– 148] → [ ] → [– 99] → [ ]

4 [268] → [– 136] → [ ] → [– 48] → [ ]

5 [517] → [– 178] → [ ] → [– 129] → [ ]

Find the missing number for each question below.

6 402 – □ = 295   **7** 614 – □ = 386   **8** 3000 – □ = 1978

9 5000 – □ = 2982   **10** 2017 – □ = 979   **11** 1005 – □ = 887

3 3024 – □ = 1993   **3** 824 – □ = 399   **3** 9000 – □ = 3785

Examples: *Partition into 10s and units.*   *Break 6, 7, 8, 9 into '5 and a bit.'*

$$46 + 18 = (40 + 6) + (10 + 8)$$ $$27 + 36 = (25 + 2) + (35 + 1)$$
$$= (40 + 10) + (6 + 8)$$ $$= (25 + 35) + (2 + 1)$$
$$= 50 + 14 = 64$$ $$= 60 + 3 = 63$$

Use the nearest multiple of 10 and adjust.

$$37 + 39 = 37 + 40 - 1$$ $$54 - 19 = 54 - 20 + 1$$
$$= 77 - 1$$ $$= 34 + 1$$
$$= 76$$ $$= 35$$

M

Work out

1 $9 + 5$ **2** $8 + 6$ **3** $14 + 12$ **4** $16 + 17$ **5** $12 + 29$

6 $25 + 18$ **7** $19 + 45$ **8** $32 + 65$ **9** $35 + 28$ **10** $34 + 39$

11 $43 - 16$ **12** $62 - 39$ **13** $57 - 41$ **14** $71 - 49$ **15** $46 - 29$

16 $62 - 19$ **17** $103 - 48$ **18** $133 - 69$ **19** $185 - 76$ **20** $201 - 88$

21 Coy and complete each number chain.

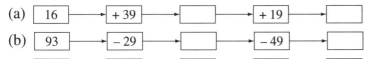

(a) $16 \longrightarrow +39 \longrightarrow \boxed{} \longrightarrow +19 \longrightarrow \boxed{}$

(b) $93 \longrightarrow -29 \longrightarrow \boxed{} \longrightarrow -49 \longrightarrow \boxed{}$

(c) $38 \longrightarrow +43 \longrightarrow \boxed{} \longrightarrow -19 \longrightarrow \boxed{}$

E

Copy and complete the addition squares.

1

+	28	37	16	19
9				
51				
18				
39				

2

+	65	36	48	73
17				
59				
28				
64				

Copy and complete

3 $\boxed{} - 38 = 215$ **4** $\boxed{} - 71 = 328$ **5** $48 + \boxed{} = 339$

6 $\boxed{} - 69 = 346$ **7** $62 + \boxed{} = 283$ **8** $\boxed{} - 48 = 561$

9 $\boxed{} + 57 = 394$ **10** $\boxed{} + 75 = 216$ **11** $\boxed{} - 89 = 472$

ADDING AND SUBTRACTING 2 ────────────────

M

Work out

1 165
   + 48

2 584
   + 219

3 462
    37
   + 86

4 276
    519
   + 137

5 466
    58
   + 273

6 64
   − 27

7 83
   − 49

8 419
   − 263

9 700
   − 486

10 1164
    − 636

11 7 + 29 + 146

12 385 + 49 + 164

13 824 + 139 + 46

14 7009 + 387

15 612 − 383

16 582 − 196

17 400 − 262

18 863 − 479

19 1872 − 696

20 Three hundred and seven take away fifty-nine.

21 Six hundred and fifty-two take away twenty-six.

22 Four hundred and thirty-seven take away sixty-nine.

E

Work out

1 3.85
   − 1.67

2 2.93
   − 1.06

3 4.6
   − 1.42

4 5.12
   − 2.68

5 7.36
   − 3.09

6 £6.24 + £3.93

7 £4.19 + £2.58

8 £6.82 − £4

9 £3.38 + £4 + £2.86

10 £6.47 + 68 p + £3.54

11 £5.17 − 68 p

12 Ron has £8. He spends £1.45 on a drink. How much money does he have left?

13 Wayne weighs 63.6 kg. He loses 5.8 kg in weight. How much does he weigh now?

14 Find the sum of

(a) 17.9 and 6.5

(b) 13.2, 8.7 and 16.3

(c) 2.28, 1.6 and 3.17

15 Find the differences between

(a) 15.4 and 7.8

(b) 6.3 and 2.48

(c) 1.4 and 0.84

16 Marie weighs 49.8 kg, Joe weighs 31.6 kg and Luke weighs 83.2 kg. Luke weighs more than Marie and Joe combined. By how much does he weigh more?

MULTIPLYING WHOLE NUMBERS AND DECIMALS

M

Work out

1 382
× 4

2 573
× 6

3 659
× 9

4 2186
× 3

5 3205
× 7

6 4316
× 6

7 2463
× 8

8 1485
× 5

9 5617
× 9

10 2894
× 8

11 Pete bought a cello for £1643. His sister bought a piano which cost her six times more than the cello. How much did she pay for the piano?

12 Which is larger and by how much? 2148×7 or 1984×9

13 Put these answers in order of size, starting with the smallest.

A 3218×6 B 2497×8 C 3368×5

E

Work out

1 1.8×4

2 3.6×6

3 2.4×9

4 5.9×5

5 3.2×8

6 6.7×7

7 4.6×3

8 2.8×7

9 Jake cycles 4.9 km. Helen cycles six times further than Jake. How far does Helen cycle?

10 Kate uses 5.3 litres of water to wash her bike. Her mother uses seven times more water to wash her car. How much water does her mother use?

11 Which is larger and by how much? 4.8×7 or 5.3×6

12 Put these answers in order of size, starting with the smallest.

A 6.4×8 B 5.7×9 C 8.2×6

M

Work out

1 43 × 29   **2** 26 × 34   **3** 54 × 47   **4** 75 × 56

5 Copy and complete this multiplication square.

×	46	24	83
57		1368	
49			
78			

E

1 Sundeep runs 14 miles each day. How far does he run in 23 weeks?

2 A dvd costs £13. How much will 36 dvds cost?

3 Barry works in an office. Every day he recycles 58 pieces of paper. How many pieces of paper does he recycle in 63 days?

4 Andrea earns £94 each week. How much will she earn in three months (13 weeks)?

5 Ashley collects keys. Each year he collects 16 keys. How many keys would he have after 12 years?

6 38 people each have 17 pairs of shoes. How many pairs of shoes do they have in total?

7 A shop sells football shirts for £48 each. How much money does the shop get if it sells 86 football shirts?

8 27 boys each weigh 43 kg.
16 girls each weight 39 kg.
What is the total weight of all the boys and girls together?

M

1 Pencils are sold in packs of five. How many packs can be made from 17 pencils?

2 A class of 26 children is to be split into groups of 4. How many groups can be made?

3 Six wine bottles can fit into a carrier. How many carriers are needed to carry 34 wine bottles?

4 A lorry can transport up to seven cars. How many lorries are needed to transport 30 cars?

5  47 people are to be split into teams of five.

   (a) How many complete teams can be made?

   (b) How many people are left over?

6 33 people are trying to get from the cinema to a party by taxi. A taxi can carry 4 people. What is the least number of taxis needed to carry all 33 people?

7 Jordan saves £3 each week. How many weeks will it take him to save £35?

E

1 Cinema tickets cost £7. How many tickets can Donna buy with £60?

2 One lorry can collect the waste from 500 houses. How many lorries are needed to collect the waste from 4200 houses?

3 A chef needs to cook 100 Yorkshire puddings. He uses one baking tray for every 12 puddings. How many trays does he need?

4 A bus can carry 55 people. How many buses are needed to carry 300 people?

5 Terry saves £350 each month for a sofa which costs £2000. How many months will it take him to save the money?

6 How many complete weeks are there in 60 days?

7 A multipack contains 8 cans of coke. Kim wants 130 cans for a party. How many multipacks must she buy?

Examples:

$$12 \text{ r } 3 \atop 6\overline{)7^15}$$ $$71 \text{ r } 7 \atop 9\overline{)64^16}$$

M

Work out and give the remainder as a whole number.

1. $8\overline{)289}$ 2. $6\overline{)166}$ 3. $9\overline{)378}$ 4. $9\overline{)522}$

5. $6\overline{)255}$ 6. $4\overline{)94}$ 7. $7\overline{)328}$ 8. $8\overline{)413}$

9. $222 \div 6$ 10. $123 \div 9$ 11. $99 \div 8$ 12. $224 \div 8$

13. $531 \div 9$ 14. $104 \div 7$ 15. $235 \div 6$ 16. $390 \div 8$

17. £ 456 is shared equally between 8 people. How much does each person get?

Examples:

$$2.49 \atop 4\overline{)9.^19^36}$$ $$5.28 \atop 6\overline{)31.^16^48}$$

E

Work out, giving your answer as a decimal.

1. $4\overline{)12.4}$ 2. $6\overline{)28.8}$ 3. $2\overline{)6.32}$ 4. $7\overline{)37.59}$

5. $25.6 \div 4$ 6. $5.49 \div 3$ 7. $14.46 \div 6$ 8. $47.52 \div 8$

9. $25.34 \div 7$ 10. $17.12 \div 4$ 11. $68.4 \div 9$ 12. $11.88 \div 6$

Work out, giving your answer in pounds and pence.

13. £6.50 ÷ 2   14. £25.60 ÷ 5   15. £19.38 ÷ 3   16. £22.20 ÷ 6

17. £33.60 ÷ 8   18. £24.60 ÷ 4   19. £11.52 ÷ 3   20. £29.33 ÷ 7

21. Grapes cost £9.78 for 3 kg. How much does 1 kg. of grapes cost?

22. 6 magazines cost £17.34. How much does one magazine cost?

23. 7 boxes of chocolates cost £32.55. How much does one box of chocolates cost?

CALCULATOR: BRACKETS AND SQUARE ROOTS | Main Book page 201

M

Use a calculator to work out:

1 3.8 + 6.24   **2** 5.7 − 3.9   **3** 6.18 − 4.73   **4** 7.6 − 1.94

Write down each answer below in pounds and pence:

5 £6.38 + 49p   **6** £5.35 − 86p   **7** £4.19 + 87p

8 (£3.12 − 36p) × 3   **9** (£4.28 + 65p) × 5   **10** (£6.39 − 74p) × 9

11 (£13.89 + 39p) ÷ 6   **12** (£18.08 − 86p) ÷ 3   **13** (£56.11 − 75p) ÷ 8

Copy and complete the number chains below:

14 1.85 ⟶ ×7 ⟶ ☐ ⟶ ÷5 ⟶ ☐

15 4.9 ⟶ ×8 ⟶ ☐ ⟶ ÷4 ⟶ ☐

Work out:

16 (38 + 16) × (27 − 16)   **17** (63 − 16) × (28 − 12)   **18** (32 − 19) × (43 + 28)

19 (6.9 − 1.7) × (4.6 − 2.8)   **20** (1.8 + 2.9) × (3.6 + 1.8)   **21** (8.2 − 1.7) × (37 + 26)

E

Work out

1 $\sqrt{121}$ **2** $\sqrt{256}$ **3** $\sqrt{1.69}$ **4** $\sqrt{46.24}$

5 $\sqrt{144} - \sqrt{64}$ **6** $\sqrt{289} + \sqrt{36}$ **7** $\sqrt{324} - \sqrt{16}$ **8** $\sqrt{1444} - \sqrt{729}$

9 $16 \times \sqrt{196}$ **10** $\sqrt{81} \times \sqrt{361}$ **11** $7 \times \sqrt{529}$ **12** $\sqrt{625} \div \sqrt{25}$

13 Find a number which multiplies by itself to give 1156.

14

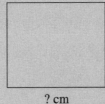

8 cm   area = 8 × 8
        = 64 cm²

8 cm

? cm   area = ☐ × ☐
        = 676 cm²
        Find the value of ☐

? cm

15 How long is one side of a square if the area is 1024 cm²?

16 Which is larger and by how much? $\left(\sqrt{225} - \sqrt{49}\right)$ or $\left(5 \times \sqrt{4}\right)$

17 Which is larger and by how much? $\left(\sqrt{961} + \sqrt{841}\right)$ or $\left(\sqrt{2304} + \sqrt{144}\right)$

18 Put these answers in order of size, starting with the smallest.

A $\sqrt{3600} \div \sqrt{400}$ B $\sqrt{1156} - \sqrt{900}$ C $\sqrt{(13 - 9)}$

UNIT 6

M

1 Change these numbers into fractions:

(a) 3% (b) 60% (c) 0.4 (d) 0.07 (e) 0.53

2 Change these numbers into percentages:

(a) $\frac{1}{10}$ (b) $\frac{19}{100}$ (c) $\frac{3}{4}$ (d) 0.09 (e) 0.8

3 Change these numbers into decimals:

(a) 6% (b) 27% (c) 30% (d) $\frac{9}{10}$ (e) $\frac{43}{100}$

4 Copy and complete this table:

fraction	$\frac{1}{4}$				$\frac{43}{100}$
decimal			0.7	0.39	
percentage		11%		20%	

E

Work out

1 10% of 60 **2** 20% of 60 **3** 40% of 80 **4** 25% of 36 **5** 5% of 40 **6** 90% of 30

7 Match each question to the correct answer.

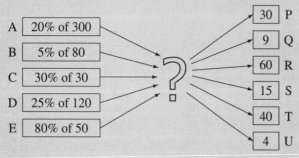

A 20% of 300
B 5% of 80
C 30% of 30
D 25% of 120
E 80% of 50

30 P
9 Q
60 R
15 S
40 T
4 U

8 What is the sale price for each item below?

(a) Computer £600 SALE 30% off

(b) Shirt £36 SALE 25% off

(c) Camera £180 SALE 20% off

(d) TV £800 SALE 10% off

(e) Bag £30 SALE 60% off

(f) Shoes £60 SALE 5% off

THE FOUR OPERATIONS 3 ────────────────

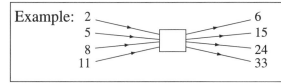

Example:
2 → 6
5 → 15
8 → 24
11 → 33

All the numbers on the left have been multiplied by 3 so the rule in the empty box is ×3

M

What rule belongs in each empty box?

1
3 → 5
5 → 7
7 → 9
9 → 11
(+)

2
2 → 8
4 → 16
6 → 24
8 → 32
(×)

3
3 → 15
6 → 30
9 → 45
12 → 60

4
4 → 1
7 → 4
10 → 7
20 → 17

5
3 → 18
5 → 30
9 → 54
15 → 90

6
2 → 9
6 → 13
8 → 15
10 → 17

What number belongs in the empty box?

7 [ ] → + 6 → 18

8 [ ] → − 9 → 14

9 [ ] → − 12 → 25

10 [ ] → ÷ 3 → 5

11 [ ] → × 6 → 30

12 [ ] → × 8 → 48

E

What rule belongs in each empty box?

1
19 → 5
30 → 16
21 → 7
42 → 28

2
7 → 36
10 → 39
19 → 48
24 → 53

3
4 → 32
7 → 56
9 → 72
20 → 160

4
5 → 30
7 → 42
12 → 72
15 → 90

5
30 → 12
25 → 7
43 → 25
41 → 23

6
36 → 4
63 → 7
45 → 5
72 → 8

7
5 → 35
9 → 63
20 → 140
11 → 77

8
48 → 16
60 → 28
53 → 21
71 → 39

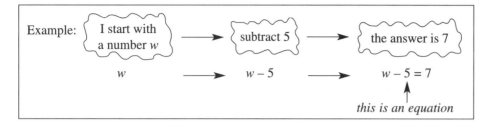

Example: I start with a number w → subtract 5 → the answer is 7

w → $w - 5$ → $w - 5 = 7$

this is an equation

M

For each question, write down an equation using the given letter.

1 I think of a number n, add 6 and get the answer 10.

2 I think of a number w, add 3 and get the answer 12.

3 I think of a number m, subtract 6 and get the answer 5.

4 I think of a number a, subtract 10 and get the answer 14.

5 I think of a number y, subtract 8 and get the answer 12.

6 I think of a number n, subtract 15 and get the answer 40.

7 I think of a number p, add 7 and get the answer 16.

8 I think of a number m, add 4 and get the answer 19.

9 I think of a number y, add 9 and get the answer 15.

10 I think of a number w, subtract 20 and get the answer 13.

11 For each equation in questions **1** to **10**, find the value of the letter.

E

1 For each question, write down an equation using the given letter.

(a) I think of a number n, multiply it by 2, add 6 and get the answer 12.

(b) I think of a number p, multiply it by 4, add 1 and get the answer 21.

(c) I think of a number y, multiply it by 3, add 4 and get the answer 13.

(d) I think of a number m, multiply it by 6, subtract 4 and get the answer 26.

(e) I think of a number w, multiply it by 5, subtract 9 and get the answer 6.

2 Find the value of n in each of these equations.

(a) $3n + 7 = 13$ (b) $2n + 1 = 11$ (c) $5n + 3 = 18$

(d) $2n + 8 = 12$ (e) $4n - 3 = 21$ (f) $3n - 6 = 3$

(g) $6n - 2 = 16$ (h) $3n - 7 = 8$ (i) $4n - 1 = 11$

Remember: you will keep weighing scales balanced if the same weight is added or taken away from both sides.

M

In the following, find the value of x.

1 $\boxed{x}\ \boxed{6}$ $\boxed{6}\ \boxed{6}$

2 $\boxed{x}\ \boxed{4}$ $\boxed{4}\ \boxed{2}\ \boxed{3}$

3 $\boxed{x}\ \boxed{7}$ $\boxed{5}\ \boxed{3}\ \boxed{7}$

4 $\boxed{x}\ \boxed{3}$ $\boxed{3}\ \boxed{3}\ \boxed{3}$

5 $\boxed{x}\ \boxed{5}$ $\boxed{9}$

6 $\boxed{x}\ \boxed{14}$ $\boxed{20}$

7 $\boxed{8}\ \boxed{x}$ $\boxed{10}$

8 $\boxed{x}\ \boxed{9}$ $\boxed{9}\ \boxed{6}$

9 $\boxed{12}\ \boxed{x}$ $\boxed{17}$

10 $\boxed{x}\ \boxed{14}$ $\boxed{40}$

E

Find the value of a x in each question below.

1 $\boxed{x}\ \boxed{x}\ \boxed{6}$ $\boxed{12}$

2 $\boxed{x}\ \boxed{x}\ \boxed{4}$ $\boxed{14}$

3 $\boxed{x}\ \boxed{x}\ \boxed{x}\ \boxed{3}$ $\boxed{21}$

4 $\boxed{x}\ \boxed{x}\ \boxed{9}$ $\boxed{17}$

5 $\boxed{x}\ \boxed{x}\ \boxed{x}\ \boxed{3}$ $\boxed{30}$

6 $\boxed{x}\ \boxed{x}\ \boxed{x}\ \boxed{x}\ \boxed{5}$ $\boxed{13}$

7 $\boxed{x}\ \boxed{x}\ \boxed{x}\ \boxed{9}$ $\boxed{33}$

8 $\boxed{x}\ \boxed{x}\ \boxed{7}$ $\boxed{27}$

9 $\boxed{x}\ \boxed{x}\ \boxed{x}\ \boxed{x}\ \boxed{7}$ $\boxed{23}$

10 $\boxed{x}\ \boxed{x}\ \boxed{x}\ \boxed{8}$ $\boxed{29}$

11 $\boxed{2x}+7$ $\boxed{19}$

12 $\boxed{4x}+3$ $\boxed{15}$

13 $3x + 6 = 15$ **14** $5x + 4 = 34$ **15** $2x + 1 = 11$

16 $4x + 7 = 39$ **17** $3x + 5 = 29$ **18** $5x + 8 = 53$

> Remember: $4a$ means '$4 \times a$'
> $3(a + 2)$ means '$a + 2$ then multiply by 3'

M

Find the value of each expression when $n = 4$.

1 $n + 3$ **2** $n + 6$ **3** $3n$ **4** $5n$ **5** $n - 2$

6 $6n$ **7** $2n + 1$ **8** $4n + 3$ **9** $5n - 3$ **10** $3n + 6$

11 $4(n + 2)$ **12** $3(n + 4)$ **13** $5(n - 2)$ **14** $2(n + 6)$ **15** $6(n - 3)$

Find the value of each expression when $n = 3$ and $p = 5$.

16 $n + p$ **17** $p - n$ **18** $2n + p$ **19** $3p + 2$ **20** $4n - 3$

21 $4p + 7$ **22** $3(n + 2)$ **23** $5(n - 1)$ **24** $n + p + 8$ **25** $4n + 2p$

26 $4(p + 4)$ **27** $2(n + p - 3)$ **28** $4(p + n + 6)$ **29** $4n - p$ **30** $5n - 2p$

E

Find the value of each expression when $a = 4$ and $b = 7$.

1 $2a + 3$ **2** $4b - 6$ **3** $3a + b$ **4** $2(a - 2)$ **5** $3b + a$

6 $6(b - a)$ **7** $2a + 4b$ **8** $a + 3b - 8$ **9** $9a - 3b$ **10** $(b + 3) \div 2$

11 $(a + 11) \div 5$ **12** $3(b + 4)$ **13** $5a + 3b + 7$ **14** $10a \div 8$ **15** $6(2a - 1)$

In questions **16** to **24**, $w = 4$ cm, $x = 5$ cm and $y = 9$ cm

16
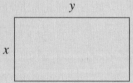
Find the perimeter

17
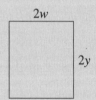
Find the perimeter

18
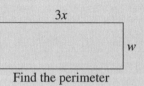
Find the perimeter

19
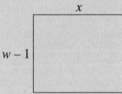
Find the perimeter

20
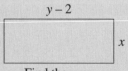
Find the *area*

21
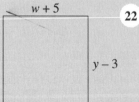
Find the *area*

22
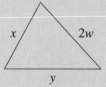
Find the perimeter

23
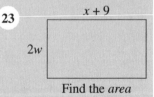
Find the *area*

24
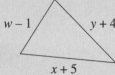
Find the perimeter

M

What number belongs in each empty box?

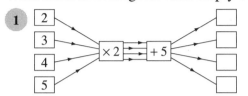

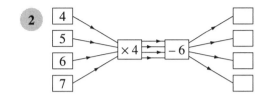

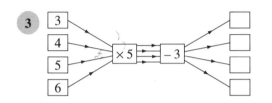

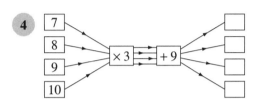

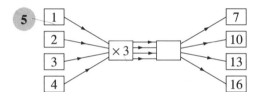

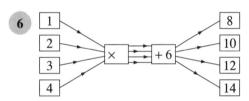

What rule belongs in each empty box in the questions below?

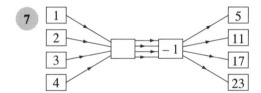

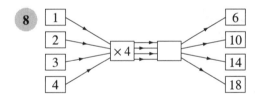

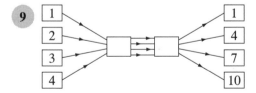

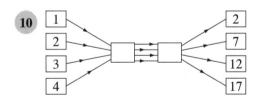

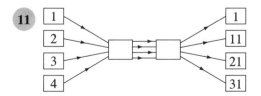

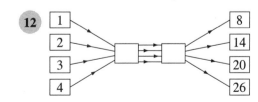

122

E

1 Here is a sequence of shapes made from sticks.

Shape number:	1	2	3
Number of sticks:	5	9	13

(a) Draw shape number 4 and count the number of sticks.

(b) Write down the rule for the number of sticks in a shape as follows:

'The number of sticks is_____times the shape number and then add_____.'

2 These dots make a sequence.

Shape number 1   Shape number 2   Shape number 3

(a) Draw shape number 4.

(b) Make a table:

shape number	1	2	3	4
number of dots	8	12	16	

(c) Write down the rule.

'The number of dots is ___ times the shape number and then add___.'

3 Here is another sequence of shapes made from sticks.

Shape number 1   Shape number 2   Shape number 3

(a) Draw shape number 4.

(b) Make a table:

shape number	1	2	3	4
number of sticks				

(c) Write down the rule.

'The number of sticks is _____ times the shape number and then add___.'

M

Use the grid to work out each message written in co-ordinates.

1. (5, 5) (4, 0) (1, 3) (2, 5) # (4, 2) (–4, 2) # (–5, –3)

    (–4, 2) (–2, 5) # (–2, –2) (1, 3) (–5, –5) (–5, –5) #

    (1, 3) # (4, –4) (1, 3) (0, 1) # (5, 5) (–2, 1) (2, 5) (4, 0) #

    (1, 3) # (5, –2) (–5, 4) (1, 3) (4, 2) (–2, 2) # (–2, 1)

    (0, 1) # (4, 0) (–2, 1) (5, –2) # (4, 0) (–2, 2) (1, 3)

    (4, 2) ? # (4, 2) (–4, 2) (–2, 5) (4, 4) !

2. (5, 5) (4, 0) (1, 3) (2, 5) # (4, 2) (–4, 2) # (–5, –3)

    (–4, 2) (–2, 5) # (–2, –2) (1, 3) (–5, –5) (–5, –5) #

    (1, 3) # (4, 2) (–2, 2) (1, 3) (4, 2) # (–5, 4) (1, 3) (–3, –4)

    (–3, –4) (–4, 2) (2, 5) ? # (–5, 4) (–4, 2) (–5, –5) (–5, –3)

    (4, 4) (–4, 2) (0, 1) !

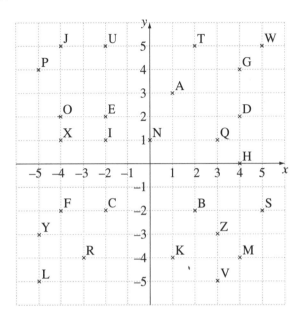

E

1. Draw the horizontal axis from –8 to 8 and the vertical axis from –8 to 8.

   Plot the points below and join them up in order. Write down what the picture is.

   (a) (–4, 0), (–2, –2), (–1, –2), (0, –4), (1, –2), (3, –2), (4, 0),

   (7, 2), (7, 3), (4, 4), (1, 4), (0, 7), (–1, 4), (–2, 4),

   (–4, 2), (–7, 4), (–5, 1), (–7, –2), (–4, 0)

   (b) (7, 5), (8, 5), (8, 6), (7, 6), (7, 5)

   (c) (6, 7), (5, 7), (5, 8), (6, 8), (6, 7)

   (d) (4, 1), (5, 1)

   (e) Draw a dot at (5, 3). Colour in the shape.

2. Draw the horizontal axis from –7 to 7 and the vertical axis from –9 to 9.

   Plot the points below and join them up in order.

   Write down what the picture is.

   (a) (0, –7), (1, –2), (1, –5), (2, –6), (1, –6), (0, –7)

   (b) (3, 3), (3, 0), (5, 2), (6, 4), (6, 7)

   (c) (–3, 6), (–4, 6), (–4, 7), (–3, 7)

   (d) (7, –7), (6, –6), (5, –6), (5, –4), (4, –2), (3, –1), (2, 2), (3, 3),

   (4, 5), (6, 7), (5, 9), (3, 9), (2, 8), (–1, 8), (–3, 7),

   (–3, 6), (–2, 5), (0, 5), (1, 4), (–1, –1), (–1, –6), (–2, –6),

   (–3, –7), (7, –7)

   (e) (2, 8), (2, 7)

   (f) (0, 5), (1, 5). Colour in the shape.

M

Find the angles marked with the letters.

1
a $50°$

2
$145°$ b

3
$65°$ c

4
$157°$ d

5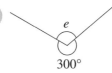
e $300°$

6
f $130°$

7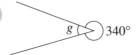
g $340°$

8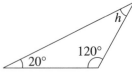
h $120°$ $20°$

9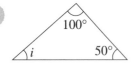
$100°$ i $50°$

10
j $69°$

11
$315°$ k

12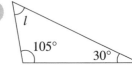
l $105°$ $30°$

E

Find the angles marked with the letters.

1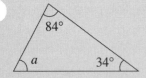
$84°$ a $34°$

2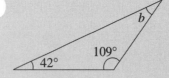
b $42°$ $109°$

3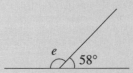
$126°$ $117°$ c

4
$316°$ d

5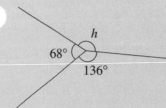
e $58°$

6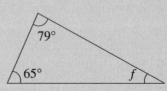
$79°$ $65°$ f

7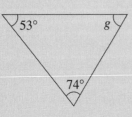
$53°$ g $74°$

8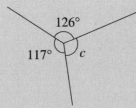
h $68°$ $136°$

9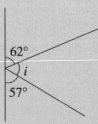
$62°$ i $57°$

10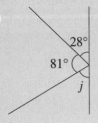
$28°$ $81°$ j

11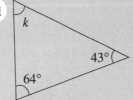
k $43°$ $64°$

12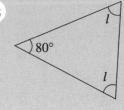
l $80°$ l

M/E

1 When the cube is made from this net, which face will be directly opposite the ▲?

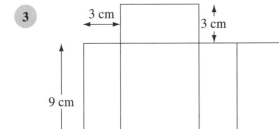

2 Name the object which can be made from this net.

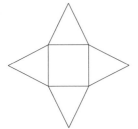

3 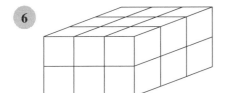 Name the object which can be made from this net.

4 Sketch a possible net for this tetrahedron (triangular pyramid).

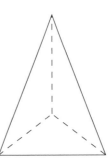

5 Draw a net for a closed cuboid measuring 4 cm by 2 cm by 1 cm.

6 Draw an accurate net for this cuboid.

M

Copy the crossnumber and use the clues to complete it.

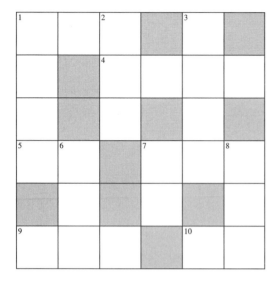

Clues across

1. $1029 - 675$

4. $368 + 3210 + 1161$

5. Pens cost £1.36 each. How many pens can you buy for £100?

7. $1458 \div (32 - 29)$

9. $7588 \div (42 - 28)$

10. Six people pay an equal share of a bill for a £138 meal. How much do they each pay?

Clues down

1. $2189 + 938$

2. 21^2

3. $83 \times (47 + 29)$

6. $14758 \div (23 + 24)$

7. $\sqrt{2116}$

8. $22^2 + 13^2$

E

Answer true or false.

1. $\sqrt{400} = 40$

2. £3 – 72p = £2.28

3. $5.9 - 4 = 1.9$

4. $60 \times 40p = £24$

5. $1.34^2 = 2.68$

6. $7.16 - 2 = 7.14$

7. Find a number which when multiplied by itself gives 1369.

8. A shop sells 163 computer games. The shop receives £5377.37. How much does a computer game cost if each game costs the same amount?

9. Copy and complete

   (a) $3.24 + \square = 5.6$

   (b) $2.93 + \square = 4.72$

   (c) $4.62 - \square = 2.8$

   (b) $6.81 - \square = 4.25$

   (e) $\square + 4.99 = 7.3$

   (f) $1.8 - \square = 0.87$

10. Molly buys 3 magazines for £2.85 each, 4 packets of crisps for 46p each and 2 bottles of water for 82p each. How much change will Molly get from a £20 note?